SECRET BEAUTY

Diane H. Irons

INTERNATIONAL IMAGE PRESS

Secret Beauty

ISBN 0-9639394-1-6

Printed in the United States of America
10 9 8 7 6 5 4 3 2 1

Published by:
International Image Press
196 Main Street
Wakefield, Massachusetts 01880-1823
(617) 246-7215
Order line: 1-800-230-9959

Library of Congress Catalog Card Number: 96-94027

Also By Diane Irons
The REAL Secrets of Beauty

To David

My best friend through the years
And the tears

Disclaimer: The author of this book does not dispense medical advice or prescribe the use of any technique as a form of treatment for physical or medical problems without the advice of a physician, either directly or indirectly. The intent of the author is only to offer information of a general nature, and to report on the results of interviews and research. In the event you use any of the information contained in this book for yourself, which is your constitutional right, the author and the publisher assume no responsibility for your actions.

TABLE OF CONTENTS

Chapter One

Attitude. Fake it til you make it!

You Are What You Think You Are

First rule: I have worked with women
with attitude. They are the women you see
on the street, the movie screen, the top magazines.
They are not the most beautiful
women I know, but they certainly think
highly of themselves. That is the only difference.
Before you start throwing this
book, cursing me out (or worse), you need
to know that there are some gorgeous creatures
hanging on to some very old myths.
They are the women I lecture who tell me
that they are "displaced housewives". Their
houses are kept in better condition than their own
"inner houses". They told me horror stories of
"throwing the baby out with the bath water", that is letting all their beauty/health/
diet regimes go because they were too "self indulgent". These women let things
go because they were too confusing, too complicated, too time-consuming, or
just too expensive. I heard these stories time after time, and I knew that this
was not so. Not only is it not necessary to give yourself up to love someone
else, but it is only when you love yourself that you can give to others.

TAKE TIME
Create time for yourself by setting the alarm clock 30 minutes earlier.
Begin rituals for yourself that become as important as eating and breathing. If you
don't have enough time during the day, take it from the minutes wasted on phone calls,
grocery shopping, or TV surfing.

KEEP IT SIMPLE
Begin a "house cleaning" on your body, closet, handbag, cosmetics, and anything else
that keeps you from feeling good about yourself and your life.

STAND UP STRAIGHT
This sounds so ridiculously simple, but it's one of the top traits of those women we admire.
Stand against a wall with head, shoulder blades, and heels touching, and fanny pushed into the
wall. Walk away without changing this position. This is how you begin your attitude
adjustment.

While you're adjusting, pick up those bra straps. That will help both those drooping shoulders
and droopy breasts.

MAKE AN EFFORT
You owe it to your self-esteem, your family, and friends to try. After all, you don't like
to look at a mess all day. Don't you love good art? Become your own canvas, and
recreate yourself.

BE THE STAR OF YOUR OWN SHOW
YOU should be what people notice. Your cosmetics and clothes should not compete for
attention with each other, or with you. Wear the basics, but with your own style.
If you like the color red, use it as a consistent accent piece in your wardrobe. Perhaps
you collect pins or bracelets? Show them off, but not all at once.

HAVE IT YOUR WAY
After years of telling us what to wear and how to wear it, designers have finally given in
to the acceptance that we as women will dance to our own drummer. Now we can finally
sigh with relief at hemlines. If you have great legs, show them off. Are you pear shaped?
Accentuate that waist and choose a long elegant look.

BELIEVE YOUR MIRROR

Most of us believe only what others tell us, not what we see in the mirror. That's why we desperately seek compliments. "Beauties" rely on their mirror, and believe everything they see. When they see great hair, they enjoy their "great hair" day. They don't concentrate on the two pounds they gained from that dessert.

DON'T BE SO MODEST

While we are encouraged to try and look our best, we're not supposed to admit that we're trying. Going that "extra yard" for beauty is thought of as vanity. In addition, some women worry that they may attract the wrong kind of attention. Wallflowers belong on walls.

DON'T ACT OR DRESS YOUR AGE

Every single beautiful woman I have interviewed possessed the same trait: agelessness. If I hadn't known their backgrounds, I would have been hard pressed to put a number on these great women. You know who these women are: you see them in a magazine or on TV. You know she's about your age, but she looks so much "better". Don't necessarily cluck "LIFT". That's not always true. Where to start? Pick up a magazine that might be geared to a different audience. Shop a different store or department than is your usual route. Find a mentor, someone whose style you admire to help you along the way.

START A JOURNAL

The first step to finding your way back to YOU is to start a daily journal. Keep your daily activities and thoughts as a reliable thermometer to your self-esteem. Use it to keep track of what you're eating, wearing, and feeling.

SET GOALS

Don't overwhelm yourself in your transformation. Set standards and goals in small steps. This is especially important if you've somehow lost yourself along the way. It could be as small as "I will lose 5 pounds by the end of the month" or "I will spend one hour a day for beauty". Sit back and see yourself as slimmer, happier, or more assertive.

FIND YOUR ENERGY LEVEL

Every person has their own clock. Don't rely on clocks to tell you when to eat, when to rest, etc. Let your body do the talking. It will tell you what it needs.

NO BRAINER

Have one or two outfits that you know look terrific, and require no thought.
Keep no more than 5 cosmetics that can take you out the door and don't have to be
color coordinated. Keep one overcoat that will look stylish and hide anything!

KEEP MOVING

Don't stay frozen in time This is such an easy place to get stuck. Keep a look that is
absolutely YOURS, but keep reinventing that look to keep up with the times. You
know who is guilty. You've seen that woman with the Farrah Fawcett hairdo, when not
even Farrah herself has kept that look. Or better yet, that friend who was MOD in the
sixties, and still refuses to believe that the revolution is OVER! Enough said.

CHANGE YOUR VOCABULARY

Replace words that you see in the media like: younger, thinner, firmer, smarter, sexier,
and change those words to just one: BETTER. You are changing your attitude because
you just want to look BETTER!

I DOUBLE DARE YOU

Remember that game we used to play as children? Whether it's just getting a manicure,
changing your hair color, just a little something new and different can give a brand new
mind set. Oh yes, of course, you CAN always change it back if you don't like it.

LEARN TO FORGIVE

This is the first step back to self-acceptance. When you break your diet? That just means
you are human. Forgive yourself. When you overspend a bit, maybe that's what
you needed today. And while you're at it...learn to forgive others. There are times when
even the most well-meaning person will hurt our feelings. Don't dwell on it. It will end up
with a binge or worse. You can't afford the hours of darkness that it can create. Get
on with your life.

MEDITATION IS A BEAUTY RITUAL

I have had the pleasure to work with some big names. Each of these great stars has
had the ability to go into some kind of trance when sitting behind that mirror. This is
a concept that I have found very relaxing. You don't really need an hour in a dark
room with candles to get the benefits of meditation. Simply use your beauty rituals:
applying make up, giving yourself a hair treatment, or just bathing. I hope that this
book will teach you to turn your entire psyche around as well as your physical looks.

Chapter two

Skin Secrets

It all begins from within!!

Water....water....everywhere.

On your face!
In your body!

Water is the #1 beauty treatment
favored by beauties across the board.

You cannot create beauty without a clean,
clear palette.

Forget the expensive stuff.
If you don't drink at least 8 to 10 glasses
of water a day, you are depriving yourself
of the best beauty treatment on earth.

Your AM Regime

1. CLEANSING

The first rule of beautiful skin is to stop overcleansing! This bad habit is unique to women in this country. Your morning routine should be nothing more than reactivating last night's moisturizer with a splash of warm water. Most beautiful women whose skin is a standout, do not OVER SCRUB their skin. If you absolutely do not feel "clean" without a little soap, wash your face with milk. Purchase "long shelf life" milk from the grocery store. Just keep it on your bathroom counter, and apply it full strength from the container. Milk is a lactic acid, and will gently peel away that top layer of dead skin to bring back that radiance, glow, and fresh appearance. If you prefer, use some powdered milk mixed with a little water. Just pour about a teaspoon of the powdered milk into your palm, and add enough water to make a soft paste. Pay special attention to the sides of the nose. Rub gently and rinse. Don't spend a lot for cleansing lotions, creams, and soaps.

2. TONING

This is your second step, and an important one. The purpose of using a toner is to remove residue soaps and oils. You can spend a lot for a toner (up to $20.00 at cosmetic counters) or you can do what models do. We carry around lemons. They are refreshing, and more potent than silly toners that contain only a little lemon, but a lot of chemicals.

Other inexpensive alternatives:
Rosewater
Witch hazel
Liquid boric acid
Or try this delightful recipe!

TEA TONIC
Mix 2 teaspoons of green or chamomile tea with 1/2 cup water.
Saturate a cotton ball and apply to face.
There's no need to rinse this or any toner off.

3. MOISTURIZING

I am so happy to tell you this: It is not necessary to spend a lot of money for a good moisturizer. Save your money and stick to the basics. Drugstores are a great outlet for basic moisturizers. Look for these key ingredients:

LIPIDS: Listed as ceramides, cerebrosides, or sphingolipids.
ESSENTIAL FATTY ACIDS: Listed as sunflower oil, grapeseed oil, primrose oil
SUNSCREEN
ANTIOXIDANTS
ALPHA HYDROXY ACIDS: glycolic, lactic, or tannic acids

DON'T BUY A VITAMIN E OR A ADDED MOISTURIZER

Break open a vitamin E or Vitamin A tablet (purchase the most potent formula for your money) and add it to your moisturizer. Gives you more bang for your buck.

THE SUN IS YOUR SKIN'S ENEMY

You should always make sun protection a priority in your regime. Use a sunscreen formulated for your face along with your moisturizer. Much of our aging; rough skin, wrinkles, age spots, etc., are really the results of too much sun. Apply to face, neck, and hands.

ADD WATER

You'll find any moisturizer more effective when applied to slightly damp skin. It forms a thin film to trap moisture in the skin.

YOUR PM REGIME

This is the most important time to take care of your skin. This is the time of day that your face is away from makeup, dirt, pollution, etc. and is free to rejuvenate. Your nighttime regime is also effective and useful in destressing your entire psyche to prepare you for the best treatment of all: beauty sleep.

1. CLEANSE

Make it easy on your skin (and your pocketbook) by using one product to remove makeup and dirt. If your skin is dry, use a lotion or cream based product that leaves behind emollients (it will feel like a light film). If your skin is normal to oily use a gel cleanser or a mild facial soap. Even though your skin may be very oily, be sure to use a gentle soap like Neutrogena or Dove. NEVER USE A DEODORANT SOAP ON YOUR FACE OR NECK!

2. EXFOLIATE

I can't overstate the need for this step. It gets the blood flowing into the face as well as remove grime. Exfoliation keeps your pores clear to keep away blemishes and black heads.

Here's what to use:

Take a packet of table sugar and gently rub into the crevices of your face.

Use instant oatmeal mixed with water and create a paste. I like to use instant oatmeal on my face and old fashioned oatmeal to exfoliate the entire body.

Rub sea salt all over the body and face. You'll find it absolutely invigorating!!

3. MASKS

My ideal face mask is my favorite investigative reporting story. I had been told that those very expensive spas that charge you hundreds for an "herbal wrap" were using mud. Okay, we have all heard of clay masks. Clay (mud is what it is) is perfect for detoxifying the skin. What I discovered is those so-called "mud treatments" use none other than good old fashioned KITTY LITTER. The catch is that the bag must be marked "100% Natural Clay". It cannot contain any additives or clumping materials. What I've also found is that this type of kitty litter is the cheapest.

Here's how to use it:
Take about a tablespoon of the dried clay and reconstitute it with a small amount of water. Mud is mud is mud!! I don't care if it comes from the great *Springs of Italy* (and if it does you'll spend about $60.00 a jar), or from your local grocery store. At less than $2.00 a bag, detoxify your entire body with it. I have worked with the most fabulous celebrities who swear by my kitty litter facial, including top makeup artists. Although they love the kitty litter facial, they know that their clients may be a little reticent. What they do is pour the kitty litter into an attractive container,

and tell their clients that they are in for a very "special" treatment. Of course everyone raves about how great it feels, etc., and then they hear that it's KITTY LITTER. I have demonstrated this several times on national TV shows and not one person has ever told me that it felt anything but absolutely refreshing.

OTHER FACE MASKS:

MAYONNAISE
Apply whole egg mayonnaise for about 20 minutes.
Rinse with cool water.

PEACH & BRANDY
Mash up a peach (ripe or canned) and mix with a tablespoon
of brandy. Leave on for 20 minutes.

TOMATO MASK
For oily skin, mash up a ripe tomato and leave on 20 minutes.

ULTIMATE CLEANSING MASK
Grind 1 cup of oatmeal to a powder
Add: 3 drops of almond oil
1/2 cup milk
1 egg white
Blend together and rinse off after 20 minutes

BANANA MASH
Mash up a very ripe banana
Add just enough honey to make a soft pulp
Apply to hair & face
This is such a great firming mask that movie stars have been
putting it in their bras as a bust firming concoction
Just make sure that you don't use a lace bra!
It could get a little messy!

HONEY MASK
Apply pure honey straight from the bottle
Leave on 15 minutes or until dry.

Top Secret Tips

To revitalize and nourish the skin:
Soak whole green beans or lentils overnight. Mash and add a small amount of honey. Apply over face and neck. Leave on 5 minutes.

Tone up tired skin:
Make up a smooth pulp of crushed cucumbers and gently pat onto face. This facial is fabulous for oily skin and clogged pores.

Apply Pepto Bismol to face. Let set until dry.

Use Milk of Magnesia straight from the bottle. Leave on 5 minutes.

Save the water from cooked vegetables and used it as an enriched face rinse.

Mix 1/4 cup vodka with lemon. Dab on with cotton swab.

Cleansing:
Watermelon juice is an excellent cleanser for dry skin and is an excellent fruit acid to reduce wrinkles.

To get the most from your facial cleanser, rub it between your hands before applying. This action heats up the product, making it easier to spread on the face

Make a paste of clove oil (a natural astringent), eucalyptus (decongestant), and chamomile (maintains pigment of skin). Massage into the skin and rinse.

Bathing

Add some baking soda to your bath (half a box will do) to soothe skin itching and irritation.

Use Epsom Salts (1/2 pound) to relax muscles and relieve swelling.

Try some instant oatmeal (or grind regular/one minute) to get rid of sunburn.

Apple cider vinegar in the bath will invigorate the body and fight fatigue.

Adding a spoonful of honey is said to help insomnia.

Combine a cup of instant milk powder with 3 drops of almond oil. Soak for 15 minutes, then use a coarse wash cloth or loofah to exfoliate dead skin.

Do you feel a cold coming on? A teaspoon of mustard powder added to a hot bath could cure it.

Orange slices in the bath beat any amount you could spend on aroma therapy.

Moisturizing

You'll find good cheap moisturizers at equestrian shops, food, and health stores.

Bag balm is an emollient used to soothe cow's udders. This stuff is wonderful on chapped lips and as extra protection during cold weather on hands and face.

Hoofmaker as it sounds, was originally intended as a hoof conditioner. However it softens cuticles, heels, and other rough spots.

Wheat germ oil keeps the skin elastic and prevents stretch marks.

Crisco is used by many women and even hospitals to add moisture. It's great for psoriasis and eczema. Hospitals disguise it as cream "C".

Kalaya Oil is derived from a flightless bird (the emu), and helps trap moisture and lessen the signs of aging.

EYES

Thin <u>cucumber</u> slices used as compresses help sore, puffy ey(

<u>Potato</u> slices (raw) have potassium to take away darkness un(

Cheap <u>tea bags</u> (make sure that they're cool or cold to the touch) on the eyes make good eye refreshers because of the tannic acid. Don't use herbal tea bags. They just don't work as well.

KNEES AND ELBOWS

Skin on knees, elbows, and above the heel can easily look discolored and very dead. Here's a bleaching mask that really works! Don't you dare wear a short skirt without trying this first.

> Add the juice of 3 lemons to 1 cup of powdered milk
> and enough water to make a thick paste. Leave on
> for 20 minutes and scrub off with a loofah or sponge.

CELLULITE

We know now that diet works and thigh creams don't. So what else can we do? Here are 8 simple steps:

1. Eat lots of fresh fruit and vegetables (preferably raw).
2. Keep away from processed foods.
3. Drink lots of water to clean cells of toxins.
   **Stay away from carbonated beverages (even low calorie)
4. Use only a little olive oil and lemon juice as dressings.
5. Avoid alcohol, which negatively affects the liver, the body's main detoxifier and filter.
6. Try to walk or jog at least 3 times a week for 30 minutes.
7. Scrub the skin with a bristle brush or loofah. Brush in slow sweeps, always towards the heart. They sell gloves and mitts to do this, but don't waste your money. Try to do this at least 5 minutes a day.
8. Massage your cellulite areas firmly every day with any inexpensive body cream. Look for ingredients like horse chestnut, caffeine, ivy, and algae, which all accelerate fluid loss and rev up circulation.

QUICK SKIN PICK UP

Do you need a quick glow to your skin and an all over healthier look?
Bend over at the waist, as far as you can possibly go, and hold to the count of 30.
Scientists have proven that this very simple stance boosts circulation to both face
and scalp, as well as speeding up the turnover of skin cells, reducing the possibility
of breakouts. Choose anytime during the day you like, because there are different
benefits morning, noon, and night.

> Morning: It helps you focus on a busy day
> Awakens the mind and body
>
> Noon: Gives you that midday boost
>
> Night: Helps you unwind and gets your heart rate and
> breathing back where it should be.

Try to get your head in the proximity of your knees. It's okay to bend your
knees until you get used to the position. Steady the stance by clasping hands
behind the back.

TEA TREE OIL

Use this gentle antiseptic over a 5% salicylic acid (available in stores in pads)
to heal and soothe blemishes.

FADE CREAM

Make your own potion to lighten age spots and sun-damaged upper chest.
Mix juice of 1 lemon, 1 lime, 2 tablespoons honey, and 2 ounces of plain yogurt.
Gently massage into spots. Use once a week.

FACE LIFT

There are ways to lift your face both on a cumulative and temporary basis.
For years models, actors, and actresses have been relying on the Shark's Liver Oil
and Yeast found in hemorrhoidal creams. These are the very same ingredients
that are found in very expensive "firming" creams found at cosmetic counters.
Just what these creams do for those other "cheeks" (takes down the swelling and
shrinks tissues) they do for those undereye bags, droopy jowls, etc. Makeup artists
won't do a makeover without it, rock stars, actresses, and other entertainers won't
go on the road without a big supply, and many of those big names that you think

have gone under the knife have been using it for years. If you object to the medicinal smell, simply mix it with a little of your regular moisturizer. If you do need to use it and "go", just dab a little perfume in front of each ear to diffuse any signs. I interviewed a very handsome actor in his mid fifties, and could not get over how great he looked. However, I was aware of a certain aroma wafting from his face. If you really want to "pour it on", I would suggest that you use it only at night in the privacy of your own bedroom.

If you are heading out to a special event, and want to appear "years younger", then I suggest this quick fix.

Take an egg white and beat it to a froth. Apply to face paying special attention to eye area, chin, and jaw. Let it dry (should take only 5 to 10 minutes), and lightly rinse off. Voila! Don't waste your money on those temporary lifting creams. This egg white" lift" is as least as good if not better than anything I've tried on the market today.

> "However you live it will show on your face"
>
> ....anonymous

Chapter Three

Hair Secrets

A GOOD HAIR DAY

So what do you want from your hair? You probably want it to behave. You
want it to have volume. You want it to shine. That's just how you decide what you
need in a hair product. The number one question I'm asked when it comes to hair:
"Is there a difference between expensive hair salon products and drugstore products
(also known as mass merchandise items)?" After all these years of research, I
still find that there are no quick answers. I have tried them all (and have the split
ends to prove it), yet have not come up with anything that beats the natural based
formulas.

Because everyone is unique, it is necessary to experiment. The key is to purchase
the smallest size available (travel sizes are ideal) and see what works. We've all
heard the big hype on horse shampoo (it does give you incredible volume), but it is
also very drying on some hair types. What good is that big vat of it going to do for
you, if it makes your hair look like a miniature haystack?

Here's what you need for your hair. And may I pray that you never again overspend
or have a "bad hair" day.

#1 Find a stylist you like and can trust with your hair.
>Ask a friend or even a stranger whose hair you admire.
>Pay a little extra to book the salon's "master" stylist.
>If you are done in less than 30 minutes, move on.
>Enter the salon with a specific game plan (take a picture along
>if you need to, but be realistic).

#2 Use a shampoo designed for your specific hair type.
>There are very specific shampoos on the market today to help you.
>Occasionally add a couple of caplets of vitamin E for extra nourishment.
>There are very good shampoos that perform more than one task.
>Use the cheapest brands to strip off the extra mousse, gels, etc.
>at least once a week.

#3 Condition according to your needs.

You probably only need to deep condition (10 to 30 minutes) once a week..

Facial moisturizer is a good hair conditioner.

If your hair is extremely dry, leave a little conditioner on your hair. It will be rubbed off during the towel-drying process.

#4 The Grand Finish.

Mousse is a good ending product for fine hair.

Gel is great for control, but should be used in very small amounts.

Hairspray should be used at least 10 inches on the sides of the head, and about 5 inches on top.

Always use your fingers as a styling aid while using these products.

Anti-aging Tip:

A part slightly off the center is a more youthful frame for the face.

In the 1700's towering hair was the ultimate fashion! It was not unusual to see women of this era coifed in styles that reached 25 inches. To top off their dizzying "dos", they loved to wear elaborate hats. The hairstyle fell along with the lovely Marie Antoinette's head towards the end of the century.

BACK TO NATURE

Egg Shampoo
Beat 2 eggs in a cup of warm water
Massage the mixture into wet hair
Leave on 5 to 10 minutes
Rinse in tepid water
Caution: If you rinse in hot water, the eggs could scramble.

For Lather
Mix an egg into your shampoo

To Thicken Hair
Add a tablespoon of powdered gelatin to your shampoo

Hair Shiners
1/4 cup lemon juice added to 1/2 cup water for light hair
1/4 cup vinegar added to 1/2 cup water for brunettes

Conditioner for Dry Hair
Mix: 1 egg
1 teaspoon honey
2 teaspoons olive oil
Apply to wet hair.
Cover with a shower cap or layer of plastic wrap.
Leave on at least 30 minutes before shampooing out.

Nourishing Hair Pack
Here's what to do with an over-ripe avocado.
Mash it up, and blend through dry hair.
Leave on 30 minutes.
Shampoo thoroughly.

NATURAL COLOR ENHANCERS

LIGHT HAIR
Brew a cup of very strong chamomile tea
Let it cool to lukewarm
Spray or comb into dry hair
Leave on about 20 minutes
Shampoo & rinse
This will give a color lift to blonde and light brown hair

DARK HAIR
Brew an expresso or other strong coffee
Add to dry hair
Leave on 30 minutes
This will add sparkling highlights to black or dark brown hair

NATURAL STYLING

Flat beer is a great styling tool. Simply put some in a spray mister (available at florist shops, hardware stores, beauty supply centers). Spritz on before setting hair. Don't worry, the smell disappears when dry. Beer also works for a tired perm or naturally curly hair that tends to droop. Here you would spritz the beer into dry hair and scrunch the style into shape.

My beautiful friends who are devout environmentalists swear to me that this works better than any hairspray. Dissolve a tablespoon of sugar into a glass of hot water. Allow to cool and use in a spray bottle.

> **MYTH: Alcohol is bad for the hair. Actually, cetyl or stearyl alcohol (in many of today's products) does not dry or damage the hair. These are harmless fatty alcohols that help condition and soften hair.**

DANDRUFF

Vitamin E caps or oil rubbed on your scalp will take away those ugly flakes.

Aloe Vera Gel applied to your entire head will work almost immediately.

Aspirin I interviewed world famous hairstylist Dusty Fleming of Beverly Hills
who provided me with the most unique dandruff shampoo.
Mash 30 aspirin tablets and mix into a bottle of any shampoo.
Shampoo as usual.

> Any strong dandruff shampoo will work
> in an emergency to remove extra color
> from chemically treated hair. Use
> it in a pinch when you occasionally
> leave your mixture on too long.

"Dry-Cleaning"
2 Tablespoons of cornstarch
or
1 tablespoon of talcum powder
Run either of these through the hair when you can't shampoo.

Hair Rules to Live By

#1. The shorter your forehead, the longer your bangs should be.

#2. Protect your hair, as well as your skin, from the sun. Use sunscreen on
hairline parts. Lip balm also works.

MORE SECRETS

To completely remove residue from hair, combine equal amounts of baking soda and shampoo. Leave on for 5 minutes.

Occasionally shampoo hair with a mild dishwashing lotion.

Condition hair with whole egg mayonnaise. Leave on at least 30 minutes.

Reactivate a style by spritzing with spring water.

Mix equal parts of 100 proof vodka and shampoo for extra shine and bounce.

To keep hair well conditioned, always brush it thoroughly before shampooing. This will allow some of the beneficial oil from your scalp to be blended through the rest of your hair.

Use a pony tail as an instant face-lift.

Here's a great way to grow hair quickly! Exfoliate your scalp in a hot, steamy bathroom. Massage your head for at least 20 minutes. This will allow the steam to penetrate the scalp and open up the pores.

Women of Color

Jojoba oil slicks back black hair beautifully!

"Glover's Mange" keeps black hair moist and encourages growth.

"African Pride" is a product made of all natural nutrients, and is great for shine

Copper and chestnut are good color options for warm or amber tones.

Darker skins look great with deep wine, red, or blue-black.

Don't blow dry hair too often. Let air dry when possible.

A paddle brush will make hair its most manageable.

Texture is key to controlling style.

Weaves should be done by experienced hands only!

CHAPTER FOUR

Making Up

Making Up is <u>Not</u> Hard to Do!

Everyone has time to make their faces BETTER. This is the key to applying any and all cosmetics. Their purpose is to make the face look more lively, interesting, younger, prettier, polished, etc. Making up your face means making you look like you, but better! Here's what you need to know to maximize your best assets while minimizing any defects. I'll show you how to do it whether you have 20 minutes or 20 seconds. You DO have time to show your best face to the world.

The Right Tools

Sponge
Powder Brush
Eyelash Curler
Blush Brush
Tweezers
Lining Brush
Contouring Brush

ALWAYS APPLY MAKEUP TO A CLEAN FACE!

For best results start fresh! Think of your face as a palette. You are the artist, and you must start with a clean slate. Your makeup will go on more smoothly, evenly, and adhere that much longer.

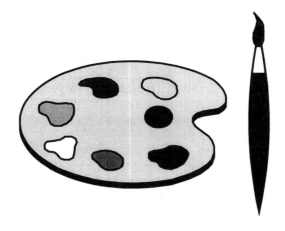

How Much Time Can You Spend On Your Makeup?

15 Minutes?
10 Minutes?
 5 Minutes?
 2 Minutes?

Your usual routine should be no more than 15 minutes flat! But what happens when you're pushed for time? The trick is to change your routine. There is no way that you can apply 15 minutes of cosmetics into a quick 5 minute routine. You CAN still look pretty great in just a couple of minutes with my streamlined techniques. There just isn't any excuse for looking "naked" "tired" or "war-painted" anymore!

The 15 Minute Face

Here's when you've got time to create a total look to take you through the day.

Foundation

Good foundation is the hardest-working cosmetic you can buy.
Choose a foundation that is right your skin type. An all-in-one foundation
that gives adequate coverage is the combination liquid /powder duo
found everywhere. I especially like the less expensive lines found in
Cover Girl, Revlon, and Loreal; less drying than the expensive brands.

Techniques for finding skin tones

Do you look good in pure white? Look for "Cool" shades
Do you look better in cream or off white? Choose "Warm" tones.
Take a coral lipstick and a pink lipstick. If your skin more closely
resembles the pink, you have pink undertones. The closer match
to the coral denotes a yellow undertone. Knowing this, you can
confidently choose your OWN color at drugstores, mass merchandisers,
etc. I can't tell you how many complaints I have received from women
who have been given the wrong color by so-called "expert's behind
those cosmetic counters. It's time to become your own consultant.
After all, who's been looking at that skin in every kind of light
imaginable for all these years? Furthermore, if you make a mistake at
the drugstore, it's easy to go the next shade (lighter or darker) or
even to blend the two at a far less exhorbidant cost.

---

1. Apply with fingers or sponge.

2. Start at the under eye area. This is where coverage is needed most.

3. Blend all over face including lips. Sweep more heavily over flaws.
Go lightly even over "good" areas to even out color.

EYEBROWS

The eyebrow is the frame for the face.
It is an easy way to "lift" the eye with a couple of quick strokes.
Some great beauties are known for their distinctive eyebrows
(think Brooke Shields, Cindy Crawford, even Joan Crawford).

Control yours with a bit of Vaseline and an old toothbrush or
an old, washed mascara wand.

Brush the brow upward and outward to define the natural line. Tweeze from under the brow. Soften the sting by rubbing the area with an ice cube. If you're completely "clueless" on what shape to make your eyebrow, cut out an an eyebrow from a magazine, and stencil it on top of your own. Tweeze accordingly.

SECRETS OF EYEBROWS

Eyebrows look best when filled in with a soft pencil or powder.
The modern brow is neither too thick nor too thin.
Undecided beauties go to a professional for their first plucking.
It's most effective to work in bright, natural light when tweezing.
Soften the look of brows by patting them lightly with powder.

Which tweezer?

Thin tip: good for grasping small, fine hairs, and getting at ingrown hairs.
Slanted tip: a versatile tweezer affording maximum control
Square tip: best usage is to remove coarse hairs or several hairs at a time.

EYES

STEP ONE:
Brush medium-toned shadow in a neutral shade over entire lid.
Deepen color in the crease and slightly above outer corner of the eye with a kohl pencil or darker shadow.
For the most natural effect, gently smudge.

STEP TWO:
Lightly powder lashes to give mascara a coat to cling to.
Line lids as close as possible with a pencil or liquid liner.
Brush first coat of mascara on. Comb through to separate hairs.
Powder over liner in shade just slightly lighter than liner.
Powder under eyes to complete look.
Add one more coat of mascara.
Smudge any hard lines with finger or Q-tip.

EYE SECRETS:

To make the white of your eyes look brighter, use a light blue pencil under eyes
******Blue eyeshadow lightly applied over works as well.

Separate clumpy eyelashes with a lash comb (available at beauty supply stores)

To get the best curl out of eyelashes, use a blow-dryer to heat an eyelash curler for about 4 seconds before using.

If you need to go from day to evening, apply an eye "foundation" before shadowing.

Use waterproof formulations when possible.

Always wipe wands off before using to avoid any clumping.

When applying mascara to bottom lashes, hold a tissue under the lash so mascara doesn't end up on skin.

Are you a complete klutz when it comes to lining your eyes? Use a shadow as a liner. Simply dampen a thin tapered brush and stroke it across powdered shadow.

Make your eyeliner last each time you sharpen it by putting it in the freezer for at least 15 minutes before sharpening. This will insure a perfect point with no crumbling.

APPLICATIONS

Wide set eyes: To make your eyes look closer together, apply deep-toned shadow to the inner halves of lids. Light-toned shadow goes on outer halves.

Close-set eyes: Open up eyes by brushing deep-toned shadow on outer halves of lids, blending from center of eyes out and up to just above the crease. Use a light shadow on inner halves of lids and just under brow bones.

LIPS

Use a neutral lip pencil rather than one that matches your lipstick.
Apply lip pencil in dots around the lip.
Connect the dots, following the natural lip line.
Fill in entire lip with pencil.
Use powder or lipstick over to seal.

CHOOSE THE BEST FORMULA!
Matte: The most lasting formulation.
Pick one that's not too drying.

Creamy: Looks the best when first applied.
Available in the widest array of colors.

Stain: This usually contains moisturizing ingredients.
Also has sunscreens added.

SECRETS OF LIPS

For a softer lip color, apply moisturizer into the lipstick.

To change the color of a lipstick, apply yellow eyeshadow on the lips as a primer. Then apply the lipstick. This will warm up any color.

Blend lip liner and lipstick together on the back of the hand.

If your lipstick tends to "bleed", apply lipstick first, then liner over it to set.

Create your own lip colors by mixing and matching.

To achieve a pouty, sexy mouth, emphasize top lip by dabbing a little gloss in the center.

To keep lipstick on while dining, keep lips off utensils. Use your lower teeth and tongue to do the work.

If you feel that your lips are unbalanced, use a lighter colored lipstick on the smaller lip.

Apply lipstick with a brush to last longer.

A little bit of red or orange in the center of the lips makes them look fuller.

After applying lipstick, pucker lips into an extreme "O". Cover your finger in a tissue, and poke it into your mouth. Twist away any excess color that will eventually come on to your teeth.

BRONZING POWDER

Ask any beauty what product she would most likely take on a deserted island, and the answer would most likely be her bronzing powder. This is the most versatile cosmetic you are likely to own. This is how you finish your face. Forget the blush! I have never seen a worse beauty blunder than misusing blush. I can't begin to tell you how many stripes I have wiped off when I have done makeovers. With the improper use of blush, you end up looking like a circus clown or major stripe zone. This is why I suggest that you use bronzing powder to both contour and add color to the face. Use it on the cheeks, down the sides of the nose, under the jawline, to take down excess oil, etc. This stuff is great! Find it in any brand in any drugstore, K-Mart, you name it. But get some. Use it. Don't go in the sun. You will get a better sun-kissed look with bronzing powder. Can you tell it's my absolute favorite cosmetic?

> Bronzer is elegant for a monochromatic look.
> Use it to shadow eyes, powder lips, etc.

THE FIVE MINUTE FACE

To look set to go in 5 minutes or under, concentrate on the basics.
Skin, eyes, and mouth.
Apply foundation as a concealer on shadows and redness.
Use a neutral lipstick on the apples of cheek and lips.
Apply liner-shadow over and under lids.
Sweep over a coat of mascara.

THE TWO MINUTE FACE

Apply tinted moisturizer on your face.
Sweep over a quick coat of mascara.
Use bronzer on eye lids, cheeks, and lips.

DON'T

When you're in a rush, don't even try the following:

Liquid eyeliner: it needs time and a steady hand.
False eyelashes: This takes precision, strips, glue, and toothpicks.
Plucking: It takes time for the redness and bumps to disappear
Lip liner: You could end up very uneven.
Foundation: Aim for a healthy glow instead.

DARKER SKINS

**Darker skin provides the perfect canvas for creating dramatic looks,
but products need to be carefully chosen and correctly applied to enhance
the skin's unique tone and texture.**

Foundation

There are over 40 shades between the lightest and darkest of black skins, so finding the
right foundation can be a real challenge. Always tests foundation on your
cheek or nose. The skin around the outside of the face is often darker than
the skin in the center. Black skin has a lot of yellow pigment, so look for
foundations with yellow undertones. Choose oil-free formulations as
darker skins reflect more light are often slightly oily. Finish with a powder
that's either transparent or slightly lighter than your skin.

Eyes

The general rule is the darker the skin, the deeper the eye color because
dark skin tends to absorb color. Use rich eye colors like golds, deep grey,
purples, russets, copper, and brown. Pale pink and beige are enhancing
highlighters. If your eyebrows are a little sparse, use dark brown or black
pencil to fill them in. Use a kohl pencil to rim your eyes, and a couple
of coats of mascara.

Lips

The same rule of "the darker the skin the darker the color" applies with the lips.
Red lips are perfect for evening, but choose reds with warm, brown tones
rather than blue undertones which tend to be too cold. Women with darker
skins usually have darker pigmentation outlining their lips so they have their own
natural lip line. If you do find that you need a lip liner, stay in the brown tones.

Blush

Peach or brown tones are most flattering to black skin. You'll find that pink shades have too
much of a blue undertone. For day use a large, soft brush to spread the color.
For evening glamour, use a brown shade a couple of tones darker than your skin color and apply
to cheek contours.

> **EXPERT TIP**
>
> **Purchase your cosmetic brushes from artist supply shops. You'll find the brushes softer, and that will make makeup go on smoother and blend better. Artist's brushes are made from natural bristles. Regular makeup brushes are usually synthetic and stiff.**
>
> Best news of all, artist's brushes cost less.
>
> $$$$$$$$$$$$$$$$$$$$$$$$$$$$$$$$$$$$

Double Duty Cosmetics

Lipsticks make a great cream blush. You'll find it a perfect way to color coordinate your face.

A nude pencil is just right to outline lips, cover blemishes, and line brows.

Eye shadow doubles as a lip primer.

Mascara can create an emergency beauty mark.

Dark brown eye liner can be used as a lip pencil.

Dry blush can be used to seal lips or change color.

Translucent powder can be used to lighten brows and seal lipstick.

CHAPTER FIVE

Model's Secrets

A Model's Bag

A model's bag is full of things you'd never dream of!
Here's a sampling of what you would find if you were to peek into the every day bag of
a working model.

Baby wipes

This is a great tool for cleansing the face, as well as removing makeup. Baby wipes are
hygienic (use them once and throw them away), and gentle to the face. You'll find that
most versions contain lanolin which is a skin softener. Purchase the convenient travel
pack to freshen up on a moment's notice. It's also useful for taking up a stain or deodorant
mark.

Hemorrhoid cream

Just think what this cream does for those other "cheeks". It shrinks and takes down the
swelling. That's just what models and other beauties use it for. It is THE secret in the
backstages of theaters, runways, etc. We use it on our sagging "under eye" area, and
down along the jaw line. It is an instant face lift, and a favorite of the "heavy party goers".

Garlic and Papaya Tablets

This is an absolute must when it's necessary to get weight off in a hurry. Garlic and
papaya tablets together act as a diuretic, and can get up to six pounds off in a couple of
days. Take 2 garlic tablets and 2 papaya tablets before breakfast, lunch, and dinner.
Eat lightly on these days, staying away from salt. There are "star" caplets out there on
the market that are priced at $100.00 & up. You can buy garlic and papaya capsules
in the local drugstore or health food store for just a couple of dollars each. Of course,
being natural supplements, they are safe.

Beef Jerky

Here is a snack that has been much maligned, and is really quite good for staying lean.
Beef jerky contains less than one gram of fat, and only 75 calories. What's especially
helpful for a model's diet is that it takes so long to chew a beef jerky (about 25 minutes).
This makes beef jerky orally gratifying. It may just keep you out of the fast food
restaurants.

Chalk

Here's a natural way to hide stains. Carry white chalk for white, colored chalk for all
the different colors of your wardrobe. I prefer that you use this over chemical stain removers,
not only for the ozone, but many fabrics have been ruined by these chemicals.

Eye redness reliever

Have I got a way for you to remove breakouts quickly!! Just the way eye redness relievers take the redness out of the eye, so does it remove redness from pimples. Squeeze out a little on a cotton swab. Hold it on the pimple for about ten to fifteen seconds, or until it disappears. Models (and the people who hire them) consider it a tragedy to get a pimple, but it's also important for you when you have that big party to be able to obliterate those little suckers. This will do it, and quickly.

Panty Hose

What do you think models do with ripped panty hose? They make their very own scrunchies. You know, those fabulous hair accessories that pull your hair back with so much style, but cost a fortune? Here's what you do: Take the panty hose leg (the more opaque, the more elasticity) and cut at two to four inch increments. You'll find these scrunchies will hold the hair beautifully without any of the stress or split ends caused by rubber bands.

Erasers

What do models do when they lose an earring back? What do models do when their earring is just too heavy to stand properly on the ear? We take the eraser off a pencil and use it to hold that earring in place. Use this when you drop the back of an earring in your office, etc. or if you find yourself in a restaurant, use a small piece of cork from your wine bottle. It works beautifully!

Hairspray

Not only will you find hairspray helpful for keeping those coifs in place, but it keeps panty hose from running. Just spray a thin film up and down your hose before each wearing. Here's another way to use hairspray that we must share with you. Should you encounter an errant wasp or other nasty in your presence, just give him (or her) a good spray. You will paralyze that sucker more quickly than any bug spray can. Did you ever dream that hairspray of yours would be so versatile?

Bag balm

Used to soften cow's udders, models have trekked bag balm or "udder" balm in their bags forever to soften lips, hands, etc. Formerly available only in Feed Supply Stores, bag balm is now available in drugstores and mass merchandisers everywhere.

Satin pillow case

A satin pillow case is necessary to keep that hairstyle in check while traveling. Not only will it be an essential when you travel, but use it at home to keep face from wrinkling.

Lemon juice

Forget the expensive toners. Models carry a reconstituted lemon in their bags to remove residue from their face. Sometimes we carry fresh lemons, but there's just so much one can stuff into those bags. Other toners of choice are: rosewater, mineral spray, and witch hazel.

Ice water

You've heard that models drink lots of water. So true! There is no better skin treatment. To get optimum benefits from water, models drink ice water. With ice water, the body needs to use over 100 calories just to warm itself to room temperature to absorb the water. You are actually using more calories than you are taking in.

Teething Rings

Placed on the eyes, teething rings will bring down any puffiness, and provide a rested, wide-awake appearance.

Spoons

Here's another way to wake up those eyes fast! Just run a spoon under very cold water. Hold the spoon over the eye for about 30 seconds. How's that for taking away that "partied all night" look!

Parsley

Parsley is rich in chlorophyll. This is a major ingredient in breath fresheners such as Clorets, Certs, etc. Breath sweetening is more effective internally than externally. There is a major advertising campaign to get people to utilize "internal breath savers". Don't spend a lot of money on these products. Just do what knowledgeable models have been doing for years. Eat the parsley on your plate, or carry dried parsley in your bag to instantly freshen your breath, and keep it fresher that much longer.

Tea

Tea keeps cavities away! Both green and black tea contain fluoride and polyphenols to prevent plaque from adhering to the tooth's surface. Models drink tea for this reason, and carry their tea bags faithfully. After models are through drinking their tea, they use their cool tea bags to refresh their eyes. Just squeeze the tea bag, and gently dab under the eye area.

Unfiltered Apple Cider Vinegar

What a versatile product! It's a great blood purifier when you put a tablespoon in a cup of hot water and drink it. You can use it as an astringent for your face and hair. It's so incredibly cheap that there is no reason to ever NOT have it on hand!

Avocado Body Butter

Models run to the various "natural" shops for this product. It gives a wonderfully smooth sheen to the skin. Even though it's a little bit sticky, models find it very worthwhile.

Origins "Sunny Delight"

This is a cream for the face that many models swear by. It's gives a healthy outdoorsy glow. Use it with or without makeup.

Olive Oil

Here is an all natural substance that models rely on when they're in the sun. Not only does it protect hair from the sun's harsh rays, but it is enhanced as a super conditioner by the sun's natural heat.

Toothbrush

Here's an old model's trick that I love! Use a toothbrush to brush your lips. Not only does it take away any chapping, but it plumps the lips up temporarily for that exquisite "pouty" look.

Tape

Models always carry double sided tape to tack up fallen hems, make quick repairs on ill fitting attire, or quick tack an accessory.

Candles

Carry around the small birthday type candles. They are great in a pinch for fixing a stubborn stuck zipper.

Colon Cleanser

You know that I don't need to elaborate, but there is something to be said for beauty to really work it needs to start "inside". Top actresses and beauties throughout history (remember Mae West with her daily enemas?) have believed in this philosophy. Cleansers come in all types from capsules to kits.

Cowbone Marrow Oil
Models are using it to rejuvenate skin. It allegedly has the benefits of a very strong amino acid. To get more information call 1-800-995-4490.

Jelly Beans
A jelly bean is a quick "pick me up", and contains only about six calories. Compare this with a Lifesaver (ten calories) or a stick of gum (up to twenty calories).

Kelp
Models carry around kelp tablets to speed up a sluggish metabolism.

Feverfew
These super beauties eat feverfew sandwiches to relieve PMS and headaches.

Rosemary Oil
Rubbed into temple, rosemary oil relieves pain by relaxing constricted muscles.

Candied Ginger
When traveling, models rely on candied ginger to prevent motion sickness.

Dandelion Tea
This is a super diuretic. You'll find it in natural supermarkets. Be sure to be careful when using this product. Stay close to a bathroom!

Brewer's Yeast
When those unfortunate eruptions occur on the face, models run for their brewer's yeast! Mixed with plain yogurt, this formula will stop a pimple from coming through. The yogurt is an anti-bacterial, while the brewer's yeast aids cell renewal.

Surgical Tape
Use surgical tape to smooth skin while you sleep. Tape an "x" between eyebrows, above the nose. During our sleeping hours, we make many expressions that can cause wrinkling and furrowing.

Lemon Peel
A great natural mouthwash that you really must try for its effectiveness over others. Combine lemon peel with witch hazel.

What do models do to get great skin?

Please note: These models must remain anonymous because of contractual agreements with clients for whom they are spokespersons.

" I drink a lot of spring water. I don't smoke, and I very rarely drink (only wine spritzers). Before a shoot, I avoid fatty foods and chocolate".

"I boil some whole milk, then let it cool down. I lift the film that forms on the surface, and apply it to my skin. After it dries, I scrub it off to exfoliate my skin."

"I drink a power punch. I mix up an equal amount of ginseng, vitamin B-12, wheat grass, and royal jelly. Not only is it great for my skin, it gives me instant energy, and helps me last through a day of shooting."
(If you don't feel like mixing up this punch, it is available at health stores.)

"I wash my face with 2 teaspoons sea salt, 1 tablespoon sesame oil, and 1/2 teaspoon lemon juice."

"I mash up a melon and leave it on my face for about 15 minutes. The melon is rich in beta carotene to combat cell damage."

"I add a tablespoon of honey to my bath. It invigorates my skin, and leaves it "silky!"

How do models stay in shape?

"I only eat twice a day. So after toast and coffee in the morning,
I choose between lunch or dinner, depending on my schedule."
I do 500 sit-ups a day followed by a five mile cycle ride or a
40-minute run.
Elle Macpherson

"I eat a breakfast of fruit, tea, and orange juice. For lunch it's usually
diced chicken breast, boiled egg, and green salad. My afternoon
snack is tomato juice, black grapes, and herbal tea. Dinner is
simply salad and steamed vegetables."
Claudia Schiffer

"My breakfast is cereal with banana and skimmed milk. Pasta or
salad is usually lunch; sushi, brown rice, and vegetables for dinner.
Dairy products go right on my rear end, so I avoid them".
Cindy Crawford

Most models are vegetarians or eat
little meat, sticking to chicken and fish.

SECRETS OF TAKING A GREAT PICTURE
(Strike a pose!)

Years of taking pictures have yielded a list of do's and don'ts. Whether it's for a business picture, yearbook, or family event, make your next picture session an absolute success!

What to wear: Choose solid colors, avoid patterns, which grab too much attention away from the face.

Wear black and white (heavier emphasis on black for blondes, whites for brunettes).

Avoid jewelry that would distract from the face or give away a date.

Avoid clothing that would shout out a season or trend. Pick classics.

Makeup: Don't use moisturizer under your foundation. It can look extremely "greasy" in a photo.

Use lots of powder, but make sure that it's a matte powder.

If you'll be snapped by flash photography, go heavier on makeup Flash photography bleaches out makeup.

Line lips, and then dip a Q-tip in powder and run along line. This will create a mouth that "pops" out.

Never wear frosts or odd colors.

Avoid overstyling, or big big hair. It looks too "overdone".

Chapter Six

Hands

A Secret to None

Just why would I devote an entire chapter to the grooming of hands?
Number one would be the many times I have been witness to the sabotage of a perfect look by
the unkempt appearance of raggedy nails, uneven cuticles, and more.
Secondly, for those who have the time, it is easy and fun to do manicures. Thirdly,
there are definite "tricks" that keep many of us from bothering. That's why I feel
that this chapter is important. Many CEO's have told me that they have turned
down a candidate because of sloppy care (that's men **and** women). So with
this is mind, take a few minutes and learn the secrets. Your hands are **always** showing.

The 8 Step Perfect Manicure

1. File

Using an emery board, file nails straight up at the sides. Don't file sides of nails inward.
The thinner your nail, the finer the emery board should be.

2. Cuticles

Apply cuticle softener (like Bag balm or Hoofmaker cream) to the edges of the nail.
Massage gently with fingertips.

3. Soak

Soak fingers in warm, soapy water. If fingers are discolored or dirty, take a tablet of
denture cleanser, and dissolve it in the water.

4.Trim

Using a cuticle pusher/cutter (available at drugstores) push cuticle back and cut any
excess hangnails. Don't cut "in" to your cuticle because it will only bleed.

5. Massage

Apply a moisturizer all over the hands, into the nails, and cuticles.

6.Wipe

Dip a cotton ball in an astringent (like Witch Hazel or lemon juice), and remove any
excess oil. This is necessary to allow polish to go on smoothly without bubbling.

7. Base Coat
Apply a base coat or primer, and allow to dry.

8. Final Coat
Brush on a one coat polish. Look for the many types that contain both a color and a top coat. They're just as good, and a great timesaver.

Special Problems

Brittle nails
Sun damage can cause very brittle nails. Always apply sunscreen protection
Once a week, apply an oil or cream, and wear gloves on your hands overnight.

Choosing a Nail File
One of the ways that you can ruin your nails is using the wrong nail file.
There are files for artificial nails, buffing, one way filing, and two way filing.
Here are the choices:

The "popsicle stick" file: The old standby. It's inexpensive, and great for natural nails.

The metal file: It's the practical file that can be washed and reused. It will leave edges very smooth.

The coarse file: This file has the feel of sandpaper, and is best used on artificial nails.

The two sided file: This file is practical because it has two uses. The slightly abrasive side shapes natural nails, while the smooth surface buffs and finishes them.

Thickened Nail Polish

After you've had nail polish for a while, it tends to thicken. Rather than toss it, turn the bottle upside down, and roll it in between your hands. Don't ever add nail polish remover to thickened nail polish. Although it will thin it out temporarily, it will eventually dry it out and spoil whatever is left.

When polish gets so gloppy that the colors separate, it's too old to keep, and best tossed.

Chapped Hands

Dry, chapped hands are a real problem to anyone who enjoys the outdoors, or does heavy housework. One solution is to use Bag Balm, the udder cream for cows. also a great solution is "Vermont White Salve". It's based on a formula from Germany that is unique and patented. Lots of beauties swear by their petroleum jelly as a protectant.

Sounds Fishy

When you're looking for a superior nail enamel, find the type that contains "ground up" herring scales. This "strange" ingredient is known in the industry as "natural pearl". This is what gives polish its extra shine, and causes it to stay pure longer.

Chipped Polish

Use a file and smooth out the chipped polish until the ridge is even with the nail. Apply polish to chipped area, allow to dry, and recoat entire nail.

Split Nail

Apply quick-drying glue to the split and let dry. Smooth with a file or buffer.

Smudges

Apply polish remover to smudged polish to smooth. Let it dry and follow up with a thin coat of polish.

Yellowed Nails

To prevent the discoloration that occurs from polish staining, always use a base coat.

Pale Nails

Although pale nails are hereditary, more often it is the result of poor circulation or anemia. Take an iron supplement or add iron rich foods to your diet.

Secret solution for horses and great beauties

After a day or two, polished nails tend to look a big dull. "Hoof lacquer" is the secret weapon of manicurists that keep nails looking like new. Oh yes, horse trainers have been using it for years.

Artificial nails

Although artificial nails may make your hands look more attractive, they can damage your own nails. The worst offenders are the stick-on variety, which cause some of the nail surface to get torn away when they are removed. Another problem is the glue, which can cause an allergic reaction.

Bullets and beauty

There are new products on the market today that will make a manicure last twice as long. One example is "Mega Hard" by L'oreal. This hardener contains the same hi-tech material used in bullet proof vests.

Tips and more Tips

Always try to purchase an acetone-free polish remover. Many nail problems could be solved this way.

Puncture a vitamin E capsule, and apply it to cuticles at least once a week as a conditioner.

Let fingers rest at least a day between manicures. This allows them a chance to "breathe".

Stick fingers in grapefruit when you need to whiten nails in a hurry.

Although formaldehyde has a somewhat drying effect on nails, you'll find that polish containing small amounts of it will tend to last longer.

Chapter Seven

Fashion and Style

What is Fashion?

News flash! Style is not fashion, and fashion is not style. You can wear tons of fashion for years, and never be stylish. Conversely, you can scoff as the fashion trends come and go, and be the doyen of style and good taste. Fashion changes by the minute, and we cannot take it seriously. Doing so is a sure sign of being a fashion victim. Most of the stylish women I have come across treat fashion with a degree of irreverence. You should too.

What is Style?

It's Not Being Afraid to Stand Out!

Women of style take fashion risks. They are the ones who will take a piece of clothing and wear it in a way we never dreamed it could be worn. For instance, it's the woman who will wear a classic pantsuit (maybe it's Armani!), and wear a campy tee-shirt from her latest vacation. That is the fashion risk we call "style".

Style is having a trademark, and being recognized for it. It could be something as simple as not being seen without that great black jacket. Or maybe it's that brown suede pant that's dressed up and down. Sue is a friend who seems to love the combination of navy and pink. She wears it with panache whether it's going to her son's baseball game (imagine a pink sweater, topped by a classic navy blazer, and good old blue jeans) or the symphony (she stole the show by making her appearance in a lovely navy taffeta full skirt with the most beautiful ruffled pink blouse I have ever seen).

Style is not obeying those silly fashion rules. Okay, maybe you just love faux animal prints. You've loved them and worn them when they've been the star of the runway, and when they've been the "hit" of the Salvation Army. Wearing them makes you feel good, etc. Just so you have the good sense not to wear more than one piece at a time, and not to wear these pieces at a funeral or a job interview......that my darlings, is style.

Style is knowing when to stop. Let's take that love for animal prints. The difference between style and tacky is wearing one, maybe two pieces top at a time. The secret to being well dressed is always under-dressing. This allows you to wear "distinctive" clothing that stand alone.

Style is good fit. Having a good eye for how clothes fall is key to stylish dressing. For instance, knowing where those pants should fall, how that jacket should hang, etc. Adrian is such a beautiful woman, and spends an absolute fortune on top designer names. What separates Adrian from being a woman of style is that she insists on wearing a certain size, no matter how it fits her. Somehow, she has it in her mind that she is a size eight. As any stylish woman will tell you, a Calvin Klein size eight just may be a Dana Buchman's size six.

Style is going with what works for you. If it feels comfortable, like YOU, then you're going to get a lot more wear out of it. This is a fundamental concept of style that you should live with. Even though it's right off the runway, unless you feel confident in it, leave it alone.

WHAT IS NOT STYLE

Trying to look like a different person every day.

Forcing yourself to wear something for someone else.

Mixing two seasons in one outfit.

Trying too hard to get it right.

Feeling like you're playing "dress up".

Playing it safe with one designer.

Clothes so "fitting" it's impossible to walk properly.

More than one pattern in an outfit.

The Classics

There is a backbone to fashion known as "classic" dressing. It is what allows a woman to stay stylish throughout the seasons of her life. These women are not wearing the outrageous fashions right off the runway. You won't see these women following the models in this month's magazines. The looks you see in these arenas are important in that they stimulate our interest in fashion and style. They are meant to be talked about, in just the way we talk about art. I don't think that any woman who takes her fashion too seriously will ever be anything but a fashion victim.

A Classic Wardrobe

Here is my list of classic " must haves". These are the clothes that you can keep twenty or thirty years with occasional updates for breakage, size change, or just plain "weariness".

The sheath dress
Gold hoop earrings
Black skirt
Tank top
Well cut jacket
Basic trousers
Loafers
White cotton shirt
Tank watch
Pearls
Black or white tee shirt
Cardigan sweater

Fashion Don'ts

Here is the ultimate list of unstylish items. I don't care who wears them,
how good a buy, or how good they make you feel. Steer clear!

Lace hose
Sequins during daylight
Fishnet clothing or stockings
More than two theme pieces (western, menswear, etc.)
Sleeping bag coats or jackets
Bell bottom pants
Baby-doll dresses
Any skirt shorter than 22 inches
Huge shoulder pads
Sweat shirts
Jogging suits when you're not
Dirty sneakers
Cheap fabric
Shoes with a heel higher than 3 inches
More than 2 bracelets
More than 2 earrings in each ear
Transparent clothing
Ankle bracelets
Acid washed anything
Peter pan collars
Hats or sunglasses indoors
Bra tops
Belly button showing off the beach
Clogs and skirts
Tie-dye shirts
Madras

CAMOUFLAGE DRESSING

No matter what size, age, height, weight, etc. you can look younger, thinner, better
than ever with these secrets that I use when
I have done makeovers on TV. Sometimes the producers will
just throw some wild program title at me like "I want to look ten pounds
thinner...help" or "Please let me look ten years younger."
Then I am called in to do the job, and needless to say, when
TV ratings are on the sleeve, I have my work cut out for me.
Here are my absolute best secrets for camouflage dressing.

After using these tips, you will be assured by your own transformation that not all
those you see in the magazines, TV,
movies, are anorexic or attached to their treadmills. They
are real people who know the art of accentuating the positive,
and downplaying the negative.

Dressing Thinner

1. Match your hose to your shoes. Legs look longer and thinner when hose are
   toned to skirt and shoes.

2. Pleated trousers conceal tummy bulges, so if this is your problem area stick
   to pleats.

3. An A-line skirt emphasizes body length while hiding thighs.

Dressing thinner, cont.

4. Use a shirt like a jacket or a tunic. Choose a generously cut shirt in a heavy or lined fabric. It's an elegant look over slim pants, flowing over every possible sin.

5. Dress in one color. Head to toe in one color (called monochromatic dressing) is the most slimming. If you really want to look thinner, stick to darker colors.

6. If you have a chubby neck, choose v-necklines. They create the illusion of a longer, leaner body.

7. To bring attention to the face and away from the body, wear choker and matching earrings.

8. A long jacket is a pounds parer. It can make any outfit look elegant while hiding figure flaws.

9. Choose a low heeled shoe that is cut low on the instep. Stick to a thinner heel.

10. A loosely fitted vest can hide a thick waist.

11. Use a belt gently around the waist.

12. Always wear control top pantyhose with lycra.

13. A body suit can eliminate bulge. It also gets rid of unsightly "panty-line" and fabric pulling.

14. Choose a well fitted jacket. A look that is too loose, or "boxy" tends to add pounds.

Ways to Spot a Fashion Victim

1. They buy clothes they have no intention of wearing.
2. They buy clothes without trying them on.
3. They buy more than one of the same outfit in the same color.
4. They find clothes with the tickets on them in the back of their closet.
5. They buy clothes that have nothing to do with their lifestyle, just because it's the latest rage.

GOOD JEANS

Many women feel that finding the perfect pair of jeans is like searching for the perfect man. There really is something to be said for great jeans. Women use them as scales. They feel that they're in shape when they once again can fit in their jeans.

Here's What We Like About Jeans!

1. Jeans are classless. No one can tell how much money you have by your jeans.

2. Jeans are sexy. If you get the right fit, they're more sexy to some men than lingerie.

3. There's almost no place you can't wear jeans.

4. All you do is add a blazer to look smart.

Coats

I hope everyone pays attention to their outerwear. It is
the first thing that people see about you. It can positively be the core
of a wardrobe. Don't skimp in this department. Don't you dare
wear an old worn coat if you can afford to change to a newer, fresh version.
The current selection of cuts, colors, and fabrics means that there is the
perfect coat waiting out there for you.

Look for a good cut:

You need enough room in the shoulder, sleeves, and torso. You should be
able to comfortably fit a heavy sweater or blazer underneath.

Durability:

Look for a sturdy lining. You'll find the combination of rayon-acetate lasts the
longest. Check to see that the lining is tacked down at appropriate locations.
It should be attached at the cuffs, armholes, and hem.

Proper length:

Where do you like to wear your hemlines? Make sure your coat covers the
length you are most apt to wear. Best bet: pick a coat that almost sweeps
to the ankles. This coat will get you out the door with some dignity
no matter what you're wearing underneath.

Always in Style

Peacoat
Wrap coat
Princess shape
Reefer
Military coat
Double breasted
Traditional camel

Casual Chic

Casual chic, otherwise known as weekend wear, is an easy and fun way to dress. Most days we are given the challenge of coming up with this look. The key is to look like you arrived at your look with little or no effort.

What's not casually chic

Sweats
Anything too matched
Clothes that are uncomfortable
Anything overly tailored
Grunge
Little girl looks
Stained clothing
Runs in hose
Fallen hems
Worn down shoes
Polyester
Too much jewelry
Too much perfume
Excessive makeup
Ill fitting clothing
Unironed clothing
Any kind of lines or bulges under clothing
Pants that are too short
Pants that hang over the shoe
Hose that is darker than shoes
Rips and tears (except in jeans)
Heels with casual clothing
Stirrups showing under shoes
Silver and gold mixing
Fur (fake or real)
Athletic shoes
Wedgies
Unlined soft fabrics
Anything transparent

Swimwear

I have heard more primal screams coming out of dressing rooms
at swimsuit time than at any other time of the year. It doesn't
matter what size you are, age, etc. trying on swimwear has to
rate right along with the stirrups in our doctor's offices. I'm not saying
that buying a swimsuit will ever be fun, but I can make it a little easier for
you using these secrets.

Rule #1
Go up a size.

This is not what women want to hear, but because swimsuits are made of less
fabric than other garments, they tend to run a bit smaller than regular
street clothing. A size 12 suit will be very snug on a woman who wears a size 1
dress, but will be perfect on a woman who wears a size 10. If you insist on
trying on your regular size, be sure you can bend, stretch, sit, etc. without any
discomfort or riding up to oblivion.

Rule #2
Look at the tags.

Thank the designer gods for finally listening to us. They have developed
swimwear that actually gives the illusion of having lost ten pounds. You'll see
in the tag, usually this suits are called "minimizers". Again, try them on, becaus
you may find them quite confining.

Rule #3
Don't be afraid of color.

There is no longer any reason to stick to black or navy if you're trying to give o
the illusion of slimness. Although darker colors do slim the body, vibrant shade
like purple, magenta, maroon, and green also serve this purpose. You can also
use color to accentuate the positive while hiding any negatives. For instance, i
you want to show off a terrific bosom, choose a bright color in the bodice area
with a darker bottom. Don't be afraid of lines. Vertical lines can be especially

flattering, as well as geometric shapes and polka dots. The reason is, people's eyes never rest on a specific body area. Patterns keep the eye moving.

Caring for Your Swimsuit

Hand wash after every wearing.
Do not put your suit in the dryer.
Always dry your swimsuit thoroughly before storing.
Try not to get any lotions or screens on your suit.
If you do get any creams on your suit, use shampoo to sponge off.

Working Style

We all know about dressing for success....how the image you present at
work can enhance your chances of promotion and/or a salary increase.
But that's not all there is to that story. Just putting on any structured suit will no
longer do. The suit you choose to wear sends out a distinct message.
The trick in buying a suit for a career is to find that fine balance between
fitting in as a team member while revealing your individuality. Many
employers now realize that it's the creative dressers who are more open to new
ideas than those who dress conservatively. So just how do you find the style that's
right for you without being too risky? One that suits your body shape?
Here are the secrets of a successful working wardrobe.

Choose a style that flatters your body type.

Triangle: Keep your jacket simple, yet slightly curvy.

Straight: Give the illusion of a slimmer waist with a light colored, loosely tailored jacket.
Wear it over a fitted dark top and a belt.

Pear: Choose jackets with small, soft shoulder pads to give you more shape on top.
Make sure to stay away from double-breasted jackets so that you won't be adding bulk
to your hips.

Hourglass: Sharp, masculine tailoring is not for you. Go for soft shapes and fabrics. You
can get away with a knee-length pencil skirt or well-tailored trousers.

> You should spend one week's salary on a suit each
> season. This way you build up a working wardrobe
> which should last you several years.

SHOPPING SECRETS

Ordering by Mail

Catalog shopping can be a great relief for women who just don't have time to spend in lines at malls. It's great for women who need to "fill in" from time to time. Ordering by mail is perfect for those of us who "impulse" shop, helping us to organize our thoughts and figure out what we "really" need. It's easiest to order by mail when designer names are recognizable for the quality and fit.

Some favorites:
Chadwicks
Tweeds
Spiegel
Nordstroms by Mail
Saks Fifth Avenue
Victoria's Secrets
Clifford & Wills

Shopping Laws

#1.
Try it on!
Make sure you look great from all angles of the mirror.

#2
Stick to a list!
Stay with the pieces that will fill out your wardrobe, no matter how great of a "deal" it seems, or how trendy it is.

#3
Buy for the body you have!
"It would look great if I just lost five pounds." How many of those "promises" do you have sitting in YOUR closet? By the time you've lost the weight that adorable outfit is unadorably out of style!

#4
Don't wait until the last minute to shop!
Never shop the day before an event. You are bound to make a big mistake. Of course, those last minute events do occasionally occur. Just be prepared with a basic outfit that needs only a little accessorizing.

#5
Be careful of sales!
It's only a good buy if you would pay full price for it.

#6
Always dress well, and wear makeup!
This is so important because if you have no makeup on, everything looks horrible. If you're not well-dressed, even the lowly of the low looks better than what you're wearing.

#7
Shop alone!
Well-meaning friends can talk you into a less than flattering look (the go ahead, you deserve it routine), while salespeople are just plain annoying. When followed around the store, simply explain that you need to be alone to sort through your wardrobe needs. It works every time!

DOS AND DON'TS

DOS

Start your shopping trip in your own closet.
Wear color near your face.
Raid your husband's closet.
Be careful what you wear under your clothes.
Wear white in the winter. It's called winter white.
Add a trendy touch to each season's wardrobe.
Shop in resale shops.
Keep a core of five or six basics in your wardrobe.
Pick out your favorite two or three colors and plan your wardrobe around them.
Develop a theme for your wardrobe.
Purchase items that can be worn in any season.

DON'TS

Be afraid to split up outfits.
Over accessorize.
Try to hide figure flaws in over-sized clothing.
Wear tops that display your favorite beer, cause, dog, etc.
Wear a full jacket with a full skirt.
Use more than two colors in an outfit.
Wear linen in winter.
Fix any part of your body in public.
Over spend on an item you don't absolutely love.
Send the wrong message with your clothing.
Keep your clothes so simple that you fade into the woodwork.
Buy clothing that requires constant maintenance.
Wear underwear as outerwear.

Chapter Eight

Special Occasion Glamour

How to Go from Day into Evening

Situation #1

The phone rings. That invitation comes. We are invited to that special event, but there's a problem. There will be no time to change into evening clothes.

Situation #2

The office party is upon us, and we need to look good in a hurry.

Solution #1

Wear a basic black dress, basic skirt and top, or well cut trouser outfit. Carry a few well-chosen accessories, and stronger makeup.

Solution #2

A classic white shirt can go right into the evening with a frilly skirt and rhinestone accessories.

Solution #3

A well cut pair of trousers can take on a new life with a sequined tee.

Solution #4

A black mock turtleneck can be belted with a rhinestone or grosgrain belt, and added to a satin skirt for last minute panache.

Solution #5

A basic suit jacket can go into the evening hours when paired with satin or lace slacks.

Solution #6

Take a regular day suit, and remove the blouse under the jacket. Extra skin is appropriate for the evening hours. If you feel just too "naked" then add a little lace hanky at the bodice.

What Does that Invitation Mean?

You received that invitation, and you haven't a clue about what to wear.
You've never been to an event of its' ilk, and don't know a soul you can
commiserate with on attire. Here's some guidelines:

The invitation reads "Informal"

Choose a classic look such as a sweater with flowing pants, or silk blouse with
matching silk pants. Appropriate heels would in the 2 to 3 inch range. Flats would
really not be appropriate. Keep accessories toned down.

The invitation says "City Attire"

Of course, this invitation to be proper would be taking place in or near a city.
For this event, black is always safe. A black trouser suit would be perfect.
Shoes can be 1 to 2 1/2 inch height.

It reads "Business/Cocktail"

Here's where that little black dress we all own comes in handy. Add a jacket according
to your comfort level. You can always take it off, should you find that look a bit too
business oriented.

The invitation reads "Formal"

This is the invitation that drives every woman crazy! What does formal mean?
When you get this invitation, you need to pull out that long dress or skirt.
Mid calf is only appropriate if it is very elaborate.

It's Black Tie!

When black tie is required, think formal but "understated". It's a different look
from formal in that there is more leverage. You can show up in a long dress,
but a well-fitted dress and jacket would be just as acceptable. A satin
dress or tuxedo pantsuit is perfectly fine.

Party Tricks

**After applying foundation and powder, lightly mist face with mineral water to set.

**Some beautiful party girls apply base before a bath so that the steam sets it.

**Do your manicure after your bath, when cuticles are soft.

**Always apply evening makeup under artificial rather than natural light.

**Apply powder under eyes and cheeks before applying eye shadow. It will be easier to wipe off.

**Apply eyeshadow over eyeliner to prevent smearing.

Quick Glamour

It shouldn't take all day to look extra special. Here are some quick tips for that "glam" look.

Hair

Instant Glamour

To give hair fullness and bounce, lift dry hair at the roots with a round brush. Pull it taut, and spritz with hair spray. Then blow dry hair on warm at high speed. Blowing it on warm makes hair flexible and allows you to restyle it. For even more fullness, bend forward so that head is tilted down when drying. Finish styling as usual.

Sparkling, Shining Hair

Give your hair a dazzling, party-perfect finish by spritzing it with a shine spray. There are several on the market that will do the job. Apply shine throughout dry hair, then brush through for even distribution.

Eyes

Fast frames

To give the eye definition and mystery, brush brows up to accentuate the arch. Set it with a toothbrush sprayed with hairspray. Finish off by adding a bit of white shadow under the brow. If necessary, before spraying pencil along the natural arch.

Mystery eyes

The smoky eye is the perfect look for after five. Take a black pencil or liquid liner and line both above and below the eye. Soften the look and secure it by running over lines with a lighter shadow.

Take the Plunge!

Little strappy, low-cut dresses put your flesh on show! Make sure it's
blemish free by gently exfoliating to lift off dead skin, even out skin tone,
and discourage break-outs. Toners will help keep oiliness under control so
be sure to wipe off residue with Witch Hazel or lemon.

If you do have blemished skin, don't panic! Take a concealer (make sure it's
water resistant) and pat over the area until it blends with surrounding area.
A quick pat of powder will set it in. If you have lines, smooth a firming face gel
over area (check the breast area).

Keep skin soft and silky by spraying on body oils that both scent and polish shoulders,
breasts, and upper arms. Here's a way to boost the sheen. Just mix a touch of
gold powder with the oil in the palms of your hands, then smooth it on.

Add a little bronzing powder into the cleavage, but be sure to blend well.

Glamour is attitude! It shines brightest when you're genuinely happy with yourself.

The Evening Bag

**There are two schools of thought when it comes to evening bags.
There's the person who carries as little as possible, and then there's
the lady who can't go out for the evening without throwing in the
kitchen sink. There are guidelines for both variety of party goer.
It just takes planning.**

The Minimalist
Money?
> Enough cash to hail a taxi.

Cosmetics?
> A lipstick and a compact.

What else?
> Breath mints
> A comb
> Maybe a hanky

The Pack Rat
Money?
> Not only a substantial amount of money (up to $100.00), but a credit card
> or two.

Cosmetics?
> Lipstick, foundation, blush, mascara, and liner.
> Super Glue to tack back false eyelashes.

Anything Else?
> Cell Phone
> Condoms
> Keys

Chapter Nine

The Finishing Touch

"What separates us from the animals is our ability to accessorize."

STEEL MAGNOLIAS

Clothes don't make the woman, accessories do.

Show me a well-dressed woman, and I will show you someone who knows the fine art of accessorizing. Accessories are the finishing touch that gives us our individuality, and shows us just how far we can go with just a little imagination. It is the most inexpensive way to extend a wardrobe, and the very first impression of good taste. Here's what I consider to be the most important accessories in any woman's wardrobe.

The Handbag

Forget shoes, handbags are the foremost accessory in a woman's wardrobe. The perfect handbag is never larger than 10 x 13 inches. Although it is not necessary to match a handbag to every outfit, there should be a coordination effort. Always choose the best handbag that you can possibly afford. To be well-groomed it is absolutely essential to carry the following items:

Lipstick (doubles as blush)
Compact (dual finish is best)
Notebook/pen
Wallet
Breath mints
Comb or brush
Neutral eye shadow (doubles as lip powder)
Eye liner
Tissues

This is a must have list. Of course, if there is room add these:

Mini pill box with supplies
Sewing kit
Mascara
Hair elastic
Nail file

Shoes

I never have a problem convincing women of the importance of shoes. It's the
men who wear their shoes forever, and get them soled, and resoled like they're
dealing with an old friend. It's the **type** of shoe that women
choose that can make or break a total look. Also, the care they give their
shoes are key in giving that important final touch. Scuffed heels, sloppy
fit, salt marks, can be fixed in moments. And they should be.

Style

Heels

Allow me to share an old model's trick with you. A lot of modeling is not as glamorous as
you may have been led to believe. Lower level modeling involves promotion work, trade shows,
and other jobs that mean we have to be on our feet, in high heels, looking glamorous.
How do we remain on our heels all day long without collapsing? The secret is to go up
a full size from one's regular shoe size. If you're a size eight in a loafer, then you take a size nine
in a three inch heel. This allows for the inevitable swelling that will take place during the
day. The most realistic comfort level for heels for those of you who need to look together
and polished throughout your workday is two inches or lower.

Fabric

If you can afford the rich buttery leather of a designer shoe, you will benefit in comfort and
flexibility. If it's completely out of your price range, try to stay away form man-made materials.
They don't last very long, and they are low on the comfort scale. It is impossible for a foot
to breathe in vinyl or plastic.

Suede is the fabric that will stretch out most quickly, so choose a shoe that fits you properly
at purchase. Shoes that are tight when you are being fitted, really never can become a
comfortable shoe, but suede is a slight exception.

Perhaps you have those shoes you just couldn't resist that you hoped would stretch out sitting
in your closet. Try this: Wet the inside of the shoes with an equal amount of water and
alcohol. Stuff the shoes with newspaper and leave them out to dry overnight.

Hosiery

I am here to simplify your life, so I absolutely refuse to go into this long soliloquy on what per cent of nylon versus lycra you should have in your hose for longevity. So here's the rule: Follow it, and you'll get the most bang for your buck.

> **The greater amount of lycra in your hose, the more attractive on the leg,   The more lycra means more durability and better quality.**

Hosiery Do's

Do continue to wear black opaque stockings. They are the most practical and slimming hose you will ever wear.

Do match your shoes and hose when you can. This is a very appealing look.

Do hand wash your hose in a mild detergent.

Do use reinforced toes when not wearing open toe shoes.

Do buy lots of your favorite hose when it goes on sale.

Do give your hose a quick spray of hair lacquer to resist runs.

Do throw out snagged hose. If you can't bear to do this, wear this hose only under trousers.

Hosiery Don'ts

Don't ever pull at your hose in public. Not only is it unsightly, it's a sure way to create a catch or a run.

Don't wear white hose unless you're in the nursing profession.

Don't scrimp on hose size. Your hose is more apt to run, and worse, fall down to your knees in the middle of that special event.

Don't bother with ultra sheer hose. They're not worth the money, and they're really not very attractive on less than perfect legs.

Don't wear dark hose with pastel clothing.

Don't wear opaque hose in the warmer months.

Don't bother with panties under pantyhose. It's redundant and silly. It ruins the smooth look that pantyhose affords, and it negates the point of what pantyhose is....namely panty and hose.

Don't wear dark hose and light shoes.

Don't match a red dress with red hose, green dress with green hose, etc.

Don't fall for designer names in panti-hose. They're really no better in terms of quality. The only reason would be that they carry a particular shade that you love.

Don't wear sheer hose with boots. Choose opaque or semi-sheer hose.

Secrets of Jewelry

Whenever the economy goes down the sale of accessories goes up. I wish that women would learn to keep their jewelry and their clothing purchases separate. A sequined sweater or highly embellished coat is never a good buy. Jewelry is the consummate wardrobe extender. Think of jewelry in the same way that you view cosmetics. A perfectly accessorized woman can correct her imperfections with jewelry in the very same way. In addition, the right jewelry can bring a look from okay to knock out great!

It Takes Courage!

An outfit without any jewelry is said to be like a painting without color. I couldn't agree more. The proper jewelry will enhance your looks, but many women shy away from this important wardrobe addition by the fear that they will appear "overdone".

Choosing Jewelry for Your Face Shape

When Coco Chanel said "Who wants to wear their money around their neck?" and began sporting coils of fake pearls and armfuls of bracelets, she elevated costume jewelry to high fashion and glamour. The look has lived on and grown. When choosing jewelry, it is most important to keep the shape of your face in mind.

Triangle Face: You should choose a wide earring or an earring with a fat drop.

Round Face: An oval earring will elongate your face. Also consider a long narrow drop for your particular face shape.

Square Face: A drop is your preferred shape. Do make sure that the bottom of your drop is large and round. A long oval button shape will also work for you.

Oval Face: Lucky you! You can wear just about any shape, but be aware that a very long drop will drag the face down with it. You may end up with a very tired look, or you may inadvertently "age" your face.

Jewelry at Work

In the office, jewelry can give ordinary work clothes great style. It can add some fun to an otherwise serious environment. Keep jewelry understated in the workplace. Bracelets shouldn't get in the way of writing or typing. One or two conversation pins are a statement. Several pins become a walking jewelry closet. Absolutely show your personal style at work. The right jewelry can make whatever you wear more sophisticated and noteworthy.

Jewelry Do's and Don'ts

Do

Do mix metals.
Do mix pearls with metals.
Do pile on several chains together. This look was invented by the great Coco Chanel.
Do bring daytime into evening with crystal jewelry.
Do have fun with your jewelry.
Do combine short chokers with long strands.
Do use bracelets to create cuffs.
Do add pins to your handbags, lapels, and pockets.
Do use pins as ice breakers at an event where you are not known.
Do use pins as a necklace enhance to change the look.
Do tack down a scarf with a coordinating pin.
Do dress up denim with jewelry.
Do soften the look of leather with pearls.
Do use power jewelry for evening.
Do bring a trouser suit into the evening with crystal pieces.
Do feel free to knot, double, and triple pearls.
Do add two chokers at once. It's a wonderful frame for the face, and will not shorten the neck.
Do mix real gems with fake.
Do wear a crystal mix during the day.
Do mix matte and shiny.

Jewelry Don'ts

Don't wear dangle jewelry at work.
Don't wear perfume near pearls. The oil will eat away the coating.
Don't wear jewelry in your nose.
Don't wear a big earring AND a big necklace.
Don't wear a lot of crystal or cubic zirconia during the day.
Don't wear white jewelry with white clothing.
Don't wear a daytime watch with evening attire.
Don't put a dainty ring on a large hand.
Don't be afraid to wear that heirloom.
Don't think of costume jewelry as tacky.
Don't wear pendants longer than the belt line.
Don't forget to coordinate jewelry and belt. Both are important accessories.
Don't be afraid to wear a pin or two on your shoulder to pick up your posture.
Don't wear two watches at once, even if it's a pendant/pin watch and bracelet watch.
Don't be afraid to shop flea markets for jewelry bargains.
Don't forget to clean your jewelry weekly.

> **Leave the kids' cartoon jewelry for the kids. It's absolutely impossible to play the sophisticate while wearing a Mickey Mouse watch.**

Secrets of Scarves

A scarf can double as a head wrap!
Use a scarf as a colorful belt.
Tie a large scarf around your waist, and it's a pareo.
A simple square scarf is a real face flatterer!
A scarf makes a wild fake necktie!
Fill in a suit with a scarf used as an ascot.
Tie a scarf on a purse to totally coordinate your outfit.
A small scarf makes a delightful wrist band.
A rolled scarf is a necklace.
Any hat looks more festive with the addition of a scarf.
Purchase silk fabric and make your own scarf.
Wear your scarf as a bow tie.

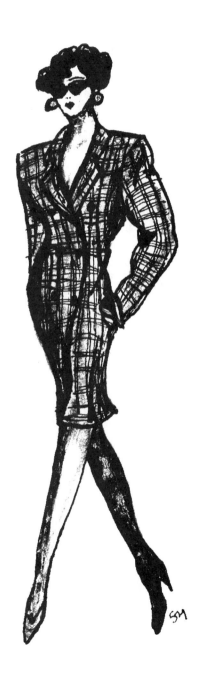

Chapter Ten

Bargains

Beauty on a Budget

It's time to take charge of your beauty and your budget. Do you truly believe that you can't have one without the other? Then this chapter will change the way you approach every aspect of your regimes. Once you take just a little extra time to read labels, and explore new merchandisers, you will be amazed at just how much you can save. Many of the name brand, cosmetic counter items you've been tied to contain the very same ingredients as the drugstore or generic versions.

Get It Wholesale!

You can find wonderful bargains without ever leaving your home. You will save both time and money by checking out these popular mail order sources.

Beauty Boutique
P.O Box #94520
Cleveland, Ohio 44101-4520
(216) 826-3008
Save up to 90% on cosmetics and toiletries. Many are discontinued items and former "gifts with purchase". Some very well known brands!

Beautiful Visions
810 South Broadway
Hicksville, NY 11801
(516) 576-9000
Save 50% to 90% on brand name cosmetics and toiletries.

Cosmetic Laboratories
339 48TH Street
New York, NY
(212) 586-4144
Skin and beauty products at completely wholesale prices. This company supplies their unlabeled cosmetics to major houses. Minimum order is $50.00.

Essential Products Co.
90 Water Street
New York, NY 10005-3587
(212) 344-4288
Save up to 90% on copy cat fragrances. Send a self-addressed stamped envelope for FREE fragrance samples.

Fragrance Express
1-800-FRAGRANCE
Discount prices on name brand fragrances including many hard to find brands.

Freeda Vitamins, Inc.
1-800-685-4980
Vitamins, minerals, and nutritional products at up to 40% savings.

Holbrook Wholesalers, Inc.
1205 Broadway
Room #204
New York, NY 10001
(212) 725-2562
Save up to 35% on Lancome products and fragrances.

L'eggs/Hanes/Bali/Playtex Outlet Catalog
(910) 744-1170
Up to 60% off panty hose, active wear, and lingerie. Call for a free catalog.

Tuli-Latus Perfumes Limited
146-36 13TH Avenue
P.O Box #422
Whitestone, NY 11357-0422
(718) 746-9337
Save up to 80% on designer impostor fragrances.

Yves Rocher Cosmetics
1-800-321-3434
They are not as inexpensive as some of the others, but they will send out 25 free samples with their catalog.

Looks That WON'T Kill (Your Budget)

A budget beauty regime doesn't mean losing out on quality or the feel-good factor.
Yes, you can look like a class act without spending a fortune, if you know which products work
Here's a list that will leave you, and your bank balance looking great!

Cleansers

They all do the same job, so why spend a fortune on a product that is only on the skin
for a few seconds? Get a cheap cream based cleanser if you have dry skin, or a gel
based cleanser for oily skin. Better yet, just wash your face with a little milk. It's much
cheaper, and better for your skin because of its lactic acid.

Toners

Spending any money at all on a toner is a big waste when for less than 30 cents, the ultimate
toner is readily available. That's a lemon, the best way to get the PH balance restored.
Need something that has no code? A little witch hazel will do just fine, or head to your
first aid department at your local pharmacy and pick up some boric acid liquid.

Moisturizer

Get an inexpensive moisturizer at the drugstore. Don't spend a penny extra for any
enrichments. Alternate between adding a vitamin A caplet in the morning, and a vitamin E
caplet at night. This is what you're hearing all the hype about. This is what they expect
you to spend $50.00 or $60.00 for. Add your own vitamins, and get a more powerful effect.
Don't spend anything extra for a sunscreen. Add a little of your own sunscreen before
moisturizing.

Cosmetics

Try to find as many cosmetics as possible that do two or more jobs. For years models
have been using lipstick as blush and eye shadow as lip powder. You can also use eye
pencil as a lip pencil to line your eyes. Unfortunately, lip pencils contain ingredients
that cannot be used in the eye area. Do create gentle contouring on the cheeks and the
sides of the nose with a neutral lip pencil.

Organize your cosmetics in an old fashioned tackle box from the local hardware store.

Hair
The best bargain for your hair is a good cut. If possible, pay extra for a master stylist. More technically advanced haircuts will last up to eight weeks.

Shampoos
There are very good brands in the drugstores. L'oreal, Clairol, and Wella offer good values along with their good names. Don't forget to enhance your shampoos with vodka (for shine) and vinegar (to remove residue), and the conditioners you can make from scratch (eggs and olive oil, mayonnaise, etc.)

Save money by using crayons or a matching mascara to touch up telltale roots

Facials
Here's a facial that won't cost one cent. Steam your face by bending over a bowl of boiling water with your favorite herbal tea.

Fade dark circles under your eyes by placing these same cold tea bags over your eyes for ten minutes.

Cook two carrots until soft, then mash. Apply to your face and let harden. This is a vitamin A mask that feels wonderful!

Try this Joan Crawford skin rejuvenator. Stick your face in a bowl of ice cubes to plump up wrinkles and close pores.

Facial Toning
Tone up your facial muscles with water! Fill up your mouth with as much water as possible. Hold it there for as long as you can. Allow the water pressure to do all the work for you.

Jut out your lower jaw. Gently raise your chin towards your nose, stretching your neck muscles. Then lower your chin back down to the starting position. Do this in the car, while talking on the phone, etc. This exercise will prevent "turkey jowl".

Free Advice

Go to your local major department store and avail yourself of their personal shopping services. It won't cost you a dime, and you'll get the unbiased opinion that you can't get from friends, commissioned sales people, or a kind significant other. Don't bother to spend money on a professional image consultant. Every one I have ever interviewed goes by a silly formula for colors, matching fabrics, and other structured stuff that is just too much work. Plus, you'll find a different opinion for every image consultant you meet. If you want several opinions, visit each of the major department stores that offer personal shopping services. Can't get out to a store? Many mail order catalogs offer free phone advice.

Home Treatments

Color and perfume your own Epsom salts for a delightful bath time experience. Get some salts at the drugstore. Store them in a big glass jar with a lid. Sprinkle in a few drops of food coloring, close the jar and shake it vigorously until the color is evenly distributed. Then pour it out onto a cookie sheet and let it dry. You can speed up things by placing it in a warm oven for a half hour if your prefer. Perfume your salts with a little perfume oil. Just add a few drops of your favorite fragrance, and shake again until there aren't any clumpy bits. Add a metal scoop and you have your very own bath treatment.

You can add sea salts and baking soda to give it a different texture.

To combat dryness, add a cup of oatmeal and tablespoon of avocado oil to a warm bath. Soak for at least 15 minutes.

While you're relaxing in the tub, increase the moisturizing effect by mashing two strawberries with two teaspoons of yogurt. Leave on your face for 15 minutes. If you have a leftover strawberry, rub it over your gums to promote healthy gums.

Remove excess oils from your face by mashing a tablespoon of pineapple and applying to face for 15 minutes before rinsing.

After shaving legs, rub a slice of cucumber over them. Cleopatra used to have her legendary skin rubbed with cooked cucumber peels.

Tips....tips....tips

Don't buy an expensive cosmetic bag. A plastic pencil case is perfect (and transparent).

To extend the life of a nail polish, clean the top of the bottle with a tissue after applying. Polish build-up allows air into the bottle and the product will evaporate.

Almond oil will stop acrylic nails form dehydrating and coming away from the nail plate.

Save on accessories by shopping girls' and teens' departments. You can save on hair accessories, costume jewelry, purses, and scarves.

Use hairspray to stop static.

Get the most out of your fragrance by applying it only to pulse points.   A lot of perfume is wasted by spraying the air.

Save leftover lipstick, and pack it down in a small paint box.

File only the tops of your nails, and your manicure will last longer.

Massage left over hair conditioner into your cuticles.

Avoid costly mistakes by creating a journal of things you own. You'll also be able to come up with creative combinations.

Explore thrift shops when you have a large block of time. Since these types of shops don't worry much about cash flow, you'll find ten times the merchandise that you would find in a regular store. It may take patience and time, but the rewards are unending for the diligent bargain hunter.

Use oversized, outdated earrings to glamorize a plain pair of pumps.

Add your own buttons to a pair of gloves for a designer look.

Add tassels to scarves for a rich style.

Cut buttons off old clothing and recycle them for other clothes.

Tips...Tips...Tips..cont.

Witch hazel makes a great hair degreaser when there's no time to shampoo.

Check to see if your insurance company will pay for sunscreen.

Peruse hardware stores for great buys on chains for pendants and belts.

Use floor wax to protect shoes and keep them shiny.

Have a clothing swap with friends and see how great your shopping "boo-boo" can look.

Use eyeshadow as a liner. Wet it down and apply with a fine brush.

Mix your own colors by combining lipsticks and eye shadows.

Shop men's and boy's departments for great buys in sweaters, shirts, and workout clothing.

Shop your own closet once a month.

Chapter Eleven

Anti-aging Secrets

Simple Ways to Resist Aging

By cutting down or avoiding the following, you can help your skin to look good:

The sun
The number one reason why our skin ages. Wear sunscreen at all times, and don't forget protective clothing.
The scalp also needs to be protected from the sun.

Smoking
Early wrinkling occurs due to reduced levels of the oxygen needed to keep skin healthy. Smoking is a prime source of oxygen deprivation.
If you are in the process of quitting smoking, drink lots of water.

Alcohol
In excess, alcohol dehydrates the body and robs its of vitamins that keep skin both healthy and glowing.
Never have an alcoholic drink without a chaser of ice water.

Improper nutrition
The modern day use of convenience foods encourages the formation of free radicals. These foods are high in processed fats and oils. Protection of the skin is possible by eating foods rich in vitamins A, C, and E. Fresh fruits and vegetables are particularly good for young skin. Supplementation may be necessary.

Stress
A constant menu of stress causes the skin to become sensitive and prone to breakouts. Regular exercise and meditation will help diffuse its effects.
Lying on a bed with your head hanging down off the side is a great destresser.

Purchases Every Aging Beauty Must Make

Three-way Mirror
Especially after 40, you must be sure that you look as good going as you do coming. Unfortunately, some of the very first signs of aging occur from behind.

Magnifying Mirror
There are things happening to your face and body that aging eyes may not see. A three to five times magnification mirror will help you to check on such exciting things as age spots, facial hair, etc.

The Right Magazines and Literature
There are a wealth of magazines and self-help books geared for women who are no longer twenty or have any wish to go back to that time. You need the magazine that tells you that it is perfectly acceptable to forgo the grunge and the rubber looks for something that may be a bit more appropriate to the "classic" beauty.

A Jump Rope
For women who are unable to get into a full exercise program, jumping rope tones arm and leg muscles while building cardiovascular endurance. Increased heart and lung performance will result in increased blood flow to the skin's surface. A good walk will do, a good run is better, but do it at least three times a week. This will also keep cellulite and varicose veins from creeping in.

Bronzing Powder
Never leave home without the youthful look of a tan. Now you don't have to. There is nothing that looks more "rested" than a tan. There's not one thing that will age you faster. Use bronzing powder liberally over the face, décolletage, and neck. It takes the years off quickly and efficiently.

> "The secret of staying young is to live honestly, eat slowly, and lie about your age."
>
> Anonymous

Makeup Tips to Look Ageless

Frosteds
Avoid any frosted cosmetics. That includes lipstick, blush, eye shadow, and glosses. There is nothing that ages or dates the face faster.

Blend...blend...blend
While you're blending, blend up! Blending makeup and skin-care products make them look more natural. Blending up gives the entire face a subtle lift.

Always line lips
Lining the lip prevents bleeding on to surrounding wrinkles. Aging lips are shrinking lips. Lining makes the lips appear larger. But be sure not to overdraw the lip line. A tightly drawn on mouth will only defeat the purpose of the line.

Keep the colors subtle
Black liner and dark shadow is too harsh. Wear medium-tone eye shadows, and matching or slightly darker liner. During the day you may want to treat the shadow as a soft liner.

Wear less
Use the least amount of foundation that you can get away with. Go heavier on the moisturizer. If it's possible, mix moisturizer and foundation together. Keep eye area moist.

Always use an eyelash curler
It opens up the eye and draws attention away from wrinkles.

Age Happily

Staying Young Starts in the Mind

You need to lead a balanced life if you want to stay young. Nurture both your emotional and intellectual life. Otherwise there is a danger that your life will be unbalanced. Give to others, of course, but don't forget to make time for yourself.

Be Positive

It's the "fake it until you make it" routine. Negative thinking can become a dangerous habit. Although the black veil routine can be mysterious and sexy in a 20 year old, in a 50 year old it just appears cranky and sad.

Seek Out Challenges

Fire up your brain cells and stay young by constantly doing new and exciting things. Once life becomes boring and routine, everything inside and outside rots.

Welcome the new advantages

There are advantages to getting old as well as drawbacks. You get more confident, and you no longer feel the need to prove yourself. The more you use your mind, the more room you will find in it.

Eat less

Scientists are discovering that the most effective way to prolong youth may be simply to eat less.

Take supplements

If you really ate all of the required vitamins and minerals, you would probably have to take in too many calories.

Techniques to Erase the Years

1. Strengthen your brows.

2. Color your hair younger and brighter.

3. Add curves or waves around the face.

4. Wear bangs.

5. Use powder sparingly.

6. Blushing is not just for cheekbones.

7. Color your nails even if they're short.

8. Get teeth cleaned more often.

9. Try colored contact lenses.

10. Loosen your hair.

11. Stay away from sleeveless.

12. Go lightly on alcohol.

Plastic Surgery

If your philosophy in life includes plastic surgery, there are a few things that you need to be aware of before searching out a reputable plastic surgeon. If you have looked in that mirror pushing this and pulling that, and you're tired of it, then you may feel that it's time. With all the new procedures available to you today, there's no reason to be afraid......just informed. Here's an idea of what you're in for:

Eyelid Surgery
The cost for an eye lift is in the area of $4, 000 to $5,000 depending on the extent of the surgery. The recovery time is about two weeks, after which you'll be able to hide the scarring with cosmetics. The eyes are often the first feature to show aging. The skin loses elasticity, there is a weakening of muscle, and fat pushes forward to shroud the eye.

Forehead Lift
This procedure will cost you between $2,000. to $4,000. and will require a recovery period of two weeks.

Liposuction
Depending on how much fat you want to remove from the body, liposuction surgery can cost anywhere from $1,000. to $7,000. Most common surgery areas are the thighs, saddlebags, inside the knees, and neck.

Chemical Face Peel
This procedure runs the range depending on the strength of the peel. Please keep in mind that a peel is for wrinkling only. It does not help with the loss of elasticity. Find a surgeon who specializes in peeling or laser surgery for the best results.

Don't Forget
Check out before and after pictures of actual results.
Don't rely too much on computer imaging. Surgeons work on real people, not machines.
Check to see that your surgeon is board certified.
Find a surgeon who will listen to your overall concerns.
Disregard anyone who will promise you the world in a basket.

Don't become a caricature of what your were at twenty or thirty. Women who are guilty of this tend to wear the look they had when they felt most attractive.

You've seen these women on the street.

They're wearing that Farrah Fawcett hair do

They have that beehive hairdo.

Their makeup is reminiscent of Hullabaloo.

Their foundation looks like they put it on with a spatula.

Update your makeup the way you update your wardrobe!

Age gracefully and you'll always be youthful!

Chapter Twelve

Secrets of Travel

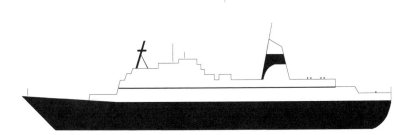

How to Pack

You can be born with a gift for it. Do it enough and you'll become an expert at it.
Packing is an art. It requires discipline, creativity, and a good deal of patience.

Luggage

When you can carry your luggage, you save time and hassles. The ideal travel wardrobe is like a well-planned itinerary. It will provide for everything you need. Whether you need it for a week or a big weekend, you want to include just what you'll wear and nothing more. You"ll need to choose items that work with each other. Choose luggage that is both light and durable. Some luggage is already heavy before anything is packed. This is the most ridiculous luggage made. Stay away from it. Modern materials are now available that weigh next to nothing and do the job beautifully. Also avoid luggage that has no bend or give to it.

Colors

This require a great deal of restraint, but stick to two colors when packing. For instance, black and ivory are two colors that work well when traveling. You'll add one more color for dimension and accenting. If you're choosing black and ivory, perhaps the third color you choose will be red for a dash of pizzazz.

Clothes

Take those few key pieces (trousers, shorts, skirt, jacket) according to the climate you are visiting, and let your accessories carry you through. Lay everything out on the bed and make up different combinations before packing.

Packing

Bulky or heavy items should always be placed at the very bottom and sides of the suitcase. This prevents them from falling down and wrinkling clothes as soon as the suitcase is picked up. Fill shoes with socks and underwear, and slip them into plastic bags to protect your clothing. Place high heels with heel toward the middle, so that they won't ruin your luggage. Plastic bags work much better than tissue paper when it comes to keeping clothes from wrinkling. Also, because they are see-through, you know where everything is. Because plastic bags are slippery, you can fit in a lot more. Perfume bottles should try to be placed inside shoes. Not only will it protect the bottle, but it also keeps the shape of the shoe.

Cosmetics

Try to find a compact beauty case. If you like to hang your cosmetics from the back of the bathroom door hook, choose a roll-type cosmetics bag. Fill your cosmetic bag with travel sized items. You should be able to go to your local department store and get sample sizes of just about every cosmetic you'll need. Seal all toiletries in a plastic bag.

Jewelry

When packing jewelry, there are tricks that every smart traveler uses. If you're planning to bring some necklaces along, just wrap them around a hair curler. Secure them with an elastic. They'll unroll perfectly......no more knots or tangles.

Other tricks

Fold long, easily wrinkling fabrics around sturdier ones. For instance, pack your elegant silk jumpsuit around your jeans.

Don't pack anything you don't wear at home.

Pack a scarf or two. You'll find this is one of the most useful travel items. You can wear it as a sarong, use it as a swimsuit cover, use it in place of a blouse to wear under suits, and even use it to strategically cover stains.

Upon arrival at your hotel, unpack everything and hang any wrinkled garments in the show to steam away wrinkling.

Always include a sewing kit, scissors, and a clothes brush or tape.

A hairdryer takes on another life when traveling. It's a quick dryer for hose, lingerie, and small stains.

The plastic bags you've packed will be used at your destination for laundry and wet suit storage.

Use a good sized tote to carry on anything you consider a necessity That usually includes eyeglasses or contact lens items, money, camera, medication, real jewelry, passport, and reading materials.

Pack a fold away bag for the souvenirs you won't be able to live without.

In the Air

Drink plenty of liquids to counteract the drying effects of "canned" air.

Wear glasses instead of contact lenses.

Pre-order a vegetarian meal.

If it's a long flight, ask for a window seat so that you'll have something to lean on while you sleep.

Grab a pillow and blanket upon boarding.

Bring a tooth brush and toothpaste for long flights.

Always wear something comfortable like an oversized sweater you can cuddle in.

Don't drink more than one glass of liquor. It's very dehydrating.

Bring slippers or slipper socks. Something to keep your feet warm when you slip off your shoes.

Special Destinations

Ski Vacations

Always wear a moisturizing sunscreen of at least 15 SPF.
Use powder foundation so that there'll be no rub-off on your clothes.
To keep color on your lips, line entire lip with pencil and finish off with a lip balm.
Don't bother with blush. The outdoors will give you a natural glow.
A high ponytail or braids will control long hair, and is perfectly okay on the slopes.
Avoid hat-head by wearing earmuffs or a headband.
Wearing a one-piece ski suit will be more slimming than separates.
Lycra will also pare off pounds.
Use extra conditioning treatments on your hair to avoid static from hats.

Sun Spots

Good sunglasses are essential for eye safety and wrinkle protection.
Wear clothes with a built-in UV block. Pure silk, high shine polyester, and terry cloth are sun blockers. Stay away from bleached cottons and crepes.
Stage your workouts in the pool. The natural buoyancy makes the muscles work harder, and feels great.
Use the beach's sand to exfoliate your skin.
Leave your hair conditioner on in the sun. It acts like a heat cap.
Sprinkle talc into shoes before wearing.
Wear cotton underclothing.
Stay cool with loose waistbands.

Chapter Thirteen

Maintaining & Organizing Secrets

Always Protect Your Investments

After spending a small fortune on your wardrobe, shoes, and accessories, it just doesn't make any sense not to keep your things in good repair. You'll end up keep them longer, and looking your very best at moment's notice. Remember, you never know when you'll need to head out the door in a hurry. You take care of your car, your kids, and your home. Why won't you give yourself the same consideration? It doesn't take that long, and it's well worth the effort.

<u>Clothes</u>

Altering clothes gives them a new life. Long skirts can be shortened; wide pants can be "taken in", and shoulder pads are easily removed.

Invest in a good clothes brush.

Remove lint from knits and woolens by shaving the surface with a razor or old panty hose.

Dry cleaning is the quickest way to pick up a tired looking garment.

Wash or dry clean clothing before you store them. Moths are less attracted to clean clothes.

When storing clothes, keep moths away by putting some dry bay leaves between layers in storage boxes, and garment bags. You'll find that they won't leave the distasteful odor found in moth balls.

Jackets must be hung to keep their shape. Stuff arms with tissue paper or newspaper.

Use plastic hangers when possible. They're better shaped than wooden or wire hangers. Wrap hangers in tissue paper to support heavier clothing.

Fold sweaters. Hanging them will cause them to mysteriously grow!

Always button and zip up clothes for proper hanging.

Shoes

Use an old fashioned rubber eraser to remove grime from suede and fabric shoes.

Use a soft cloth or brush (not wire) to loosen surface dirt.

A black felt-tip pen can color in scuff marks.

Store your boots on boot trees. If you have no room, stuff them as much as possible with newspaper.

Pull out the innersole of your shoe or boot and let it air out periodically.

Never let shoes dry near a radiator or heating duct. Too much heat may crack the leather and shrink skin.

Go easy on waterproofing and harsh chemical treatments. Some of the ones on the market today can do as much harm as good. Butcher's wax is a safe weather proofer.

To remove salt stains from boots, dampen a sponge with white vinegar. Gently blot away marks.

To rid suede of water marks, brush against the grain. Allow to dry. If it's a soft suede, fill with tissue or newspaper to keep the integrity of the suede.

Erase dark marks from pale leather by dabbing with nail polish remover.

Blot grease stains with a paper towel. Follow up by massaging with talcum powder for five minutes. Brush away with a soft brush.

Clean patent leather with a glass cleaner. Of course, the traditional "spit" routine is just as good.

Accessories

When cleaning a handbag, remove contents and stuff with newspapers.

For leather or suede gloves, stuff the fingers with paper towels or toilet paper tubes. Place the gloves on top of a soda bottle to dry.

Brush your jewelry with baking soda or toothpaste.

Use only the mildest soap on pearls.

Get your eyeglasses to stay put by dabbing clear nail polish on top of the screws. This will keep them in place.

Organization

Take your earrings, and fasten them through the holes of a button. It will keep them from getting separated.

Gather up all your pins and brooches. Decorate them on a cork bulletin board. They will be in sight and available. No more looking around in drawers for your jewels.

Use old pillows to create pin art. If you are a pin collector, use a pillow for each color theme, and you will have the most wonderful display. After all, jewelry is art.

Use a hanger to display all your necklaces. This will eliminate unnecessary tangling and mess from placing long chains in jewelry boxes.

Good Hygiene

Mix a tablespoon of witch hazel with five tablespoons of water. Add a little lemon peel, and you have a potent, inexpensive mouth wash.

Use shampoo and conditioners you never liked, but are lurking around the back of your sinks to wash your makeup brushes. Use the shampoo to soak and wash, and then rinse them with the conditioner. They will be in soft, silky shape, and will make your cosmetics flow on beautifully!

If you can smell your foundation, then throw it away. If you're on a restricted budget, purchase oil-free foundation. It lasts a lot longer.

Eye makeup has the shortest shelf life. Because eyes are so easily irritated, eye makeup contains less preservatives. You are really at risk for eye infections if you insist on keeping mascara any more than six months.

Never place your cosmetics near heat. If possible, place your cosmetics in a portable container, and store it in the refrigerator. This is very important in hot climates and warmer months.

It's not necessarily a great buy if it's in a larger container. Chances are, you'll keep it longer, allowing bacteria to build up.

How long should I keep it?

Mascara	2 to 6 months
Eyeliner	8 to 12 months
Moisturizer	2 to 3 years
Powder	3 to 4 years
Toner	1 to 2 years
Foundation	1 to 2 years
Eyeshadow	2 to 3 years
Lipstick	1 to 2 years

Cyber-Beauty

Have you the fashion and beauty information and sharing awaiting you on-line?
There is something for every taste on the web, and lots of information from experts,
magazines, and other cyber fashion-addicts. If you own a computer, all you need
is a modem that you attach to your phone, and you are good to go!!

The most popular on-line services are:

America On-line (800) 827-6364
CompuServe (800) 848-8900
Prodigy (800) PRODIGY

The fees are about $7 to $15 per month for two to five hours of service.
This is well worth it when you consider what you would spend for subscriptions to the following
magazines:

Elle

Redbook

People

Longevity

Health

Woman's Day

These are just a few of the magazines on-line. Not only will you be able to read this
month's edition, but search back to previous issues.

In cyber space (available on just about any service) you can go to several fashion pages,
talk to others in newsgroups such as:

Diet

Eating Disorders

Fashion

Health and Fitness

Models

These are groups that offer great support to those of you embarking on a diet, looking for
information on a new product, etc.

Facts about Fragrances

Perfumes don't last forever. Once you open the bottle, use it until it's empty. Limit your perfume's exposure to the air. Fragrance is very much like wine, once it's open it starts to disintegrate. Women who line their boudoirs with massive amounts of various fragrances will unfortunately find that eventually the quality will be jeopardized. Eventually some of them will sour. Once a perfume or cologne starts to smell like alcohol or vinegar, it's time to toss it.

Foods affect natural body odors and the fragrance of perfumes. That's why one scent will smell one way on a vegetarian, and another on a meat eater. Fragrances will smell differently on people who eat garlicky foods as opposed to those who eat more bland foods. Fragrance is also different at certain times of a woman's menstrual cycle. Also affecting your perfume's fragrance are vitamins, cigarettes, and certain drugs.

Every night plan to bathe in your favorite fragrance, and mend your mind from the day's stresses. Your bathroom is the one room in your home that is made for sensory pleasures. Add a little mood music, and you've created your own aroma-therapy experience. Don't forget the candles!

Chapter Fourteen

Health & Intimate Beauty

Make your own toothpaste

In my research, I've seen the most outrageous ways that women have tried to whiten their teeth. Straight from the modeling world, I have seen the use of bathroom cleansers as whiteners. Oh yes, sad but true. These young lovelies are under the misconception that they can whiten their teeth with Comet and Ajax. Not only will they wear their enamel away, but it is downright dangerous. There are some great secret recipes that will safely whiten your teeth, and not cost you an arm and a leg.

It's pretty wild, but very safe. Take burnt toast. Pound a couple of slices into a powder, add a few drops of peppermint, and voila! Healthy and whiter teeth courtesy are yours courtesy of nature.

Once a week, take one teaspoon of hydrogen peroxide mixed with a teaspoon of baking soda and brush your teeth. This formula will reduce tarter and remove coffee and tea stains.

Mix three tablespoons of baking soda with two tablespoons of salt for another highly effective teeth cleanser.

Here's two great mouthwashes:

Boil a strong cup of mint tea. Cool and use.

Mix a quarter of a cup of honey and one teaspoon of ground cloves.

Agony of the Feet

What is it about feet? Some love theirs, some love other's feet.
The truth is, most of us feel that our feet are not so wonderful. Most of
us do anything we can to hide them away. Pedicurists report that clients
usually come in with a list of apologies for their feet.   How interesting that
feet are loved or loathed. Actually, properly cared for, the foot can become
a major mark of beauty enhancement. That's exactly my point.   The foot is
the most neglected part of the anatomy. Poor feet, historically considered an
errogenous zone, it's time to rethink our habits. Consider the foot an integral
part of that commitment to intimate beauty.

Wear the proper size shoe.

When purchasing a heel of above one inch, go up a half size. There's natural
swelling that occurs that necessitates going up for the comfort of the toes.
This is one time when smaller is NOT more attractive. A "tight" shoe bulges the
foot out; not to mention what it does for the wearer's expression. A larger
shoe actually gives the foot a longer line.

Take Good Care

Use an anti-perspirant on your feet. The foot contains more sweat glands than the
under arm area. Don't waste your money on expensive foot powders and
other foot odor remedies. Not only is this cosmetically important, but it is
key in keeping bacteria at bay.

Change Shoes

Never wear the same pair of shoes two days in a row. Give them at least 24 hours a
day to air out .

Soak Your Feet

At least once a week, steep four tea bags (purchase an inexpensive brand for more
tannic acid) in two cups boiling water at least five minutes. Add two cups
of cool water. Soak for up to thirty minutes.
*Don't use herbal teas because it is the tannic acid that will cause proteins in the
skin to bond. This thickens the skin, and blocks many of its sweat pores.

Relief for Foot Problems

Bunion aches

While sitting, place a thick rubber band around
big toes. Pull big toes away from each other.
Hold for five seconds.

Foot cramps

Place cotton balls between toes and squeeze toes
together for five seconds.

Arch cramps

Sit with bare feet flat on floor. Raise heel of one foot
slowly; hold for five seconds and stretch your toes.

Lower to starting position. Switch feet and repeat.

The Healthy Breast

Wear a bra

The chest muscles don't provide enough support to go braless, no matter how small your breasts.

Keep your weight constant

Yo yo dieting can cause the breasts to sag.

Eat low fat foods

It has not been discounted that high fat foods could lead to cancer.

Exercise in the proper bra

If your breasts feel tender after a workout, you're not wearing a sports bra.
Women may actually avoid exercise needlessly if they don't have the proper breast support.

A sports bra should be made of material that prevents sweat gathering underneath and between the breasts.

Make sure that the straps don't slip while running or jumping.

Intimate Tips

Bloat

If you have a tendency towards excess bloating, don't chew gum, sip through a straw, or drink from a bottle. This causes you to swallow air, which goes to your stomach.

Baring Skin

Make sure to wash after shampooing and conditioning your hair.
Hair products leave a residue of oil on your shoulders and back.
Be sure to wear sunscreen on chest and back.

Cellulite

The way to get rid of cellulite is controversial to say the least. The cottage cheese that seems to gather on the back of the thighs and other places is best eliminated by working it off in an aerobic program. Spot exercises fail miserably. Running, walking, dancing, swimming, and skating rev up the body's metabolism for burning fat throughout the body.

The cellulite marks that are so unsightly can be diminished with massage. Don't spend a lot on thigh creams. The only ingredient in those creams that really works is caffeine. You could brew up a concoction of strong coffee and massage it in. That still is controversial. Your best bet is to take a vitamin E caplet of 1,000 units, break it open and use this to massage the area.

Sex as a health tool

If you are a victim of irregular menstrual cycles, check your sex life. Researchers have found that women who have sex every week are more likely to have regular menstrual cycles or 28 or 29 days.

Women who have sex regularly find that their skin is better. This is because the level of estrogen is raised. That may be the reason why people who are in love look the part. Increased levels of hormones also are said to cause hair to grow and shine.

Need another reason? Sex is a great stress reliever.

Sleep for Beauty

There is no doubt about it. When we don't get enough sleep, we don't look so well.
Most of us need at least eight hours of uninterrupted sleep. Tossing and turning
or awakening several times a night just doesn't cut it. Unfortunately, it's not
always easy to fall asleep and stay asleep. There are ways to put the odds on your side.

Melatonin

This is the supplement that is being called "nature's sleeping pill. Taken twenty minutes
before bedtime, melatonin is certainly worth trying. Some users have expressed concern
about "nightmares", while others have praised the "vivid dreams" they are now experiencing.
Although still controversial, this supplement seems to be working for many men and women.

Eat Early

There are several reasons not to eat past five or six. Late night eating causes lousy sleeping.
You will end up wide awake while your body is trying to digest your last meal. You
will experience heartburn if you've eaten certain foods. Plus, every successful dieter knows
that late meals are not good for weight reduction.

Get Plenty of Exercise

Although going through a rigorous workout routine just before bed can keep you awake,
regular exercise may help you to sleep longer and more soundly. If you find yourself
"wired", do some easy stretching to relax and soothe your muscles and promote sleep.

Scent Your Pillow

Add a few drops of eucalyptus (available at health stores) to promote breathing. Stuffy
nasal passages whether due to a cold or flu, or other problems can cause you to wake
up during the night. Scientists have discovered that when you have a cold, you awaken
up to a hundred times, although you may not be aware of it.

Drink Tea

Several teas on the market today have been helpful in inducing sleep. Catnip and
passion flower teas are two to try. Although chamomile tea promotes sleep, it's also
a diuretic, defeating its purpose.

Beauty Sleep...cont.

Set Your Clock

Try to go to sleep and wake up at the same time every night, including weekends. Your body will try to adjust to a regular schedule. Sleeping in on weekends will disrupt your body's inner clock.

Sleep on Your Back

An age old beauty secret that is absolutely free, and could save you dozens of wrinkles over the years. Wrinkles form on the side you're sleeping on. Sleeping on a cotton pillow sets those creases in. If you can't train yourself to remain on your back, invest in a satin pillow. Your face will slide around on the pillow, discouraging the wrinkling effect.

Keep the Temperature Down

A slightly cool room is a beauty treatment! You see, a room that is too hot can cause you to sweat. Sweating increases oil production, which will clog pores. Also make certain to sleep on (and in) bed clothes that "breathe". Cotton sheets and nightdresses are the best choices.

Use Sleep Time for Beauty Treatments

Your moisturizer will be most effective during the nighttime hours when there's not much chance that you will smear it off. Also use the sleep hours to bathe your hands and feet in special conditioners. Just be sure to wear gloves and socks of it could get messy!

Wash Off Your Makeup

Remove every big of face and eye makeup before heading to bed. Failing to do so will attract acne and bacteria.

Take a Bath

A warm bath will relax the body into a "ready for sleep" mode. Use bathing as a prelude to a night of beautiful dreams.

A Guide to Shaving

Loofah Your Legs

Try to give your legs a light scrub with a loofah before you shave them.
This will get rid of all the excess dead skin cells that may otherwise clog up your razor.

If you're using a double edge razor, then switch to a single edge.

The Bikini Area

The bikini line can be difficult to shave because the hair grows in so many different directions. Be sure to prepare the skin with water and soap. Don't stop shaving the bikini area just because the colder months have set in, and you've stopped wearing a bathing suit. Discontinuing to shave this area will cause it to become overly sensitive. So when the warmer months return, you'll literally have to "break in" that area AGAIN!

Many women choose to trim their pubic hair for purposes of good hygiene and appearance. Use caution when doing so. A small scissors is most manageable.

If you choose to shave this area, either partially or entirely, prevent itching by using a medicated powder immediately after.

Underarms

Hair also grows in different directions under the arms. Learn to shave up and down AND sideways. Always prep this area thoroughly.

Deodorants

There are more deodorants on the market than ever. Here's the skinny on deodorants. They are a big hype! Sweat is sweat, and most models use the strongest deodorant available. Look, models can lose big jobs by ruining an outfit with perspiration. Go get a man's anti-perspirant, and forget about something that's perfumed or "made for a woman".

Chapter Fifteen

Supplements for Beauty

Supplements for Weight Loss

Garcinia Cambogia

Garcinia cambogia is a yellow fruit from Southeast Asia. Used in cooking, garcinia extract is added to make meals more filling. Said to aid digestion, it contains hydroxy citric acid, which is chemically similar to the citric acid in citrus fruits.

Research conducted in the 1970s at Brandeis University, and later by Hoffmann-LaRoche (the pharmaceutical company) showed that rats fed hydroxy citrate shed twenty five per cent of their body fat in twenty two days. The rats lost body fat partly because hydroxy citric acid inhibits an enzyme that converts surplus carbohydrate calories into fat.

Now available in pill form and in bars at health food store, garcinia cambogia is taken the natural weight loss industry by storm. It controls appetite naturally, and has no side effects unlike the over the counter diet pills sold.

You'll find this product in all health food stores, some mass-merchandisers, and many drugstores.

Chromium Picolinate

Scientists have discovered that people lacking in chromium have extra weight. The supplement chromium picolinate and chromium polynicotate has been around for a few years. It is an essential dietary nutrient which plays an important role in processing fat and carbohydrates. Many users claim that it cuts sweet cravings too. You need a supplement if your diet is lacking in chromium-rich foods. These foods include mushrooms, apples, broccoli, and cheese. The recommended daily allowance is from 50 to 200 micrograms. Supplements are usually sold as 200 micrograms, or mixed with other products in varying amounts.

L-Carnitine

This supplement is reported to accelerate the benefits of chromium, leading fitness buffs and dieters to take it together. It is sold as both a separate unit, and in combination with other supplements. L-Carnitine is an amino acid, which may be in short supply in your diet. Recommended dosage is from 250 to 500 mg. daily.

Vinegar

Ancient healers have used vinegar for thousands of years.
Take two teaspoons of vinegar mixed in a glass of water at each meal.
The vinegar will help your body burn fat, rather than store it
Use any vinegar that appeals to you; apple-cider vinegar is especially good.
Vinegar is a natural storehouse of vitamins and minerals.

Supplements for the Skin

Ground Antler Tips

All of Hollywood is talking about the benefits of ground antler tips. Available in ampoules and in tablets, they do not wrestle Bambi to the ground for these valuable supplements. Deer antler tips are sloughed off naturally, seasonally. There are farms in Canada that raise deer just for their antler tips. What's the big hype on these soft velvety appendages that have been used for centuries? They strengthen the body and enhance sex drive. It reportedly works wonders on the mind and emotions.

You'll find ground antler tips in health stores, but if there's a Chinatown near you, purchase them there. You'll pay a lot less. There are a lot of herbs and supplements that are available at reasonable prices. There's a very good antler tip/ginseng combination available in ampoules that sell for about $6 or $7 a package.

Over the Counter Supplements

For those of you who use over the counter diet aids in an attempt to suppress your appetite, please note the following:

Purchase the cheapest brand, because they all contain the same basic ingredients.

Don't take more than the recommended dosage. There have been reports of strokes and deaths related to overdoses.

Supplements for a More Beautiful Life

Times have indeed changed! To get the optimum amount of vitamins and minerals for your looks, vitality, and general well-being you would have to consume too many calories during any one day. That's why supplements have become such an important part of the regimens of the world's most beautiful women. These are the supplements preferred by the beautiful women you admire on the fashion pages and small and large screen. There is no way anything you put on your body could match what you can digest. Internal beauty care is always the most beneficial.

Vitamin A

Take this supplement to regulate skin hydration, aid eyesight, and to repair skin and nails.

Vitamin B

This important vitamin keeps skin smooth, promotes hair and nail growth, and improves circulation.

Vitamin C

Available in several forms, this vitamin is quickly becoming the darling of cosmetic antioxidants. It prolongs the life of vitamin E, protects immune cells in the skin to fight off cancer and other sun-related diseases. It also has been proven to fade age spots and other pigment irregularities. Of course don't forget that vitamin C fends off colds.

Vitamin E

Known as the skin vitamin, it has properties to heal scar tissue and to neutralize damaging free radicals.

Ginkgo Biloba

Good circulation is vital to a healthy brain to supply it with the food and oxygen it needs. The ginkgo tree, derived from the oldest living tree, has many benefits. It increases alertness, improves memory, and lowers cholesterol levels. But more importantly (to our beauty) there's evidence that ginkgo may be the most potent anti-ager ever! The only problem is that there's no agreed-upon standard of the right amount to take. About 40 mg seems to be the recommended dosage from most sources I interviewed.

Beta Carotene

This vitamin A precursor protects lips in cell membranes and between skin cells f from free radical attack. In everyday language, beta carotene makes the skin stay moist, supple and youthful.

Pycnogenol

A compound from the French maritime pine, this powerful antioxidant acts in a similar way to vitamin E, but with fifty times the strength of vitamin E and twenty times the strength of vitamin C. It protects cell membranes from sun damage.

Grape Seeds

Antioxidants in grape seeds protect the thin walls of blood vessels from losing their strength, to prevent and correct the appearance of spider veins.

Echinacea

Rich in polysaccharides, echinacea helps to activate immune cells. It naturally inhibits inflammation. Widely used in Europe, take it when you feel an illness coming on.

Shitake and Kombucha Mushroom

There's been lots of talk about these mushrooms, and how they help to trigger T-cells in the secretion of interferon to boost the immune system. It's sold in many form, many beauties are attempting to make teas out of it, grow it, everything but wear it. I have heard some negatives about its safety, so do be careful. If you are able to find it in tablet form, I'd go with that.

Licorice Root

Long used in Germany, it helps with vitamin absorption and the prevention of ulcers.

Seaweed

Don't laugh. The stuff you used to avoid at the beach has many benefits. It's sold in health stores in a dry form. You can reconstitute it and put in your salads and soups as some models do. If seaweed doesn't tempt your taste buds, go for the tablets. The most popular seaweed tablets you'll find: **Dulse and Kelp.**
Take it for its rehydrating effects. Seaweed is also able to boost a sluggish thyroid.

Melatonin

A supplement, that in addition to being the ultimate natural sleeping pill, eliminates jet lag, and improves mood. It also is reported to enhance the immune system, treat a variety of diseases, and even prolong life. The biggest claims that have been reported (but as of yet unproven) is that it can reverse the aging process, fight cancers, and prevent pregnancy. Most doctors, scientists, and nutritionists agree that 3 mg is the recommended dosage. There have been reports of nightmares or vivid dreams as a side effect.

Cat's Claw

Known as the Peruvian wonder herb, cat's claw is the newest herb to come out of the ancient rain forest of the Amazon. A natural anti-oxidant, one of the major benefits is that its anti-edemic (takes down swelling).

Evening Primrose Oil

English women wouldn't live without their evening primrose oil. It has benefits that include hair restoration.

Garlic

Take the deodorized variety for lowering high blood pressure.

Lavender Oil

Use it in drop form in the bath to alleviate stress and ease headache pain.

Ginger

Take ginger as a food or a supplement to prevent/heal ulcers and to ease nausea.

Grapefruit Seed Extract

Made from the seeds and pulp of grapefruits, grapefruit seed extract is getting praise from both holistic and mainstream medical researchers. It boosts the immune system, and is proclaimed by many to be an alternative to antibiotics. It is reported to fight bacteria, viruses, and parasites, which is why it is most used for flus, colds, sore throats, and even yeast infections.

Bee Pollen

The buzz on bee pollen is that it gives you an extra energy lift. Be sure to take small doses of it at first. Some users have found that they are allergic to it. It's known as the "alternative to coffee" by holistic groups.

Ginseng

Ginseng has many health and longevity benefits. It improves energy levels and enhances mental alertness. It has immune strengthening benefits, and is able to lower cholesterol levels. It is reported to decrease the chance of heart disease, and to increase the good cholesterol levels.

Dang Gui

Also known as dong quai and tang kuei, here is one of the most versatile herbs available today. From the name, it is obvious that its origins are in Chinese medicine. It has been used to treat menstrual abnormalities (cramps, PMS) and menopausal systems. It is also useful in treating respiratory problems and even gas.

Selenium

Selenium has close metabolic interrelationships with vitamin E and aids in normal body growth. Take it when you take vitamin E.

Royal Jelly

Here is one of the most enduringly popular food supplements. Swathed in the mysteries of ancient China and the East where it was first discovered, Royal jelly in its raw state is a unique, high protein food produced by bees and fed to their offspring. Used by us as a food supplement, it is available as both a capsule and a liquid. Loyal followers prefer the liquid because it can be absorbed more quickly into the system. Oh yeah, use it to boost your energy levels.

Wheatgrass Juice

It purportedly is natural energy enhancer. It is also used in homeopathic healing of some diseases.

Spirulina

Spirulina is a micro-alga that is believed to dampen the appetite. It is inexpensive and completely natural.

Silica

Great beauties swear by silica for absolutely radiant skin, luxurious hair, and super nail growth. It builds, nourishes and revitalizes cells of the body. It also provides collagen to the body.

Co-enzyme Q-10

Produced naturally in the body, it is being hailed as a powerful weapon against heart disease. Research suggests that it also may prolong youth and brain power.
Mice given co-enzyme Q-10 remained extremely active into old age and tended to live longer than rats not given co-enzyme Q-10. The results did not come in until the rats grew old, which makes Q-10 more of an insurance policy than an overnight miracle.

Chapter Sixteen

Beauty Emergencies

What Beauty Crisis?

How do you handle a beauty emergency? You handle it quickly, and quietly.
There's not one of you out there who has not had one. You stayed too long at that
party, and it shows. Or that alarm didn't go off, and there's no time to get it
all together. Well, it happens to movie stars, models, and other celebrities we admire.
There's no worse news than being told that you've been hired for the cover
of the year when you're down with the virus of the season. What tricks of the trade
are used to handle these emergencies are waiting for you in this chapter. Use
them when you want to look you're best when you're feeling your worst.

Out Damn Spot!

Since models start their careers so very young, they are experts in blemish disguise. There
are great ways to get rid of these party poopers.

Take any **eye redness reliever** and dab a bit onto a cotton swab, and hold on the pimple.
Just the way it takes the redness out of the eye, the redness of the pimple will be gone in
less than a minute. Just be sure to apply a little extra foundation in the general area of the
pimple.

Massage a touch of **tea tree oil** around the area to anaesthetize and encourage healing. Use
a non-liquid concealer match to your foundation. Dab a little on the blemish, wait a couple
of seconds, then blend lightly with a fingertip. Dust with loose powder.

Take a little **toothpaste**, and gently dab on the pimple, blending well.

Calamine lotion will take away blemishes overnight.

Got an **ice cube** on hand? Apply it directly on the pimple for a few minutes. Follow with
a dab of hydrocortisone cream.

Covering Up a Cold Sore

There are medications for cold sores and fever blisters. If you don't have any on hand, take an aspirin, and apply (it slightly dampened) on the sore. Hold it on for about three to five minutes.

Keep the sore and surrounding area clean and dry to fight bacteria.

Eat a bland diet, and avoid chocolate, nuts, or gelatin. These foods may irritate the sore and cause further infection.

Fresh Breath Fast

If you find yourself sans mints at the dinner table, don't panic. If there is parsley on the plate, chew on it. Parsley has chlorophyll just like you'll find in "Clorets".

If you're drinking water, ask the waiter to bring it with lemon. Squeeze it into the water and drink up!

Chew some basil, ginger, or mint leaves. Or grab a ginger cookie.

Grab an apple! As you chew, you'll clean away any leftover particles of food caught between teeth.

If you're at a restaurant, ask the waiter to bring you some baking soda. Run to the rest room, and rub it over your teeth and tongue.

> **To help teeth look whiter instantly, use a blue-based lipstick.**
> **Good choices: true red or plum**

Puffy Eyes

Run a spoon under cold water, and apply to eyes briefly. If your whole face is swollen, open the freezer door and count to one hundred.

Lie down and place plastic ice cubes or teething rings on eyes for about 20 seconds. Tap area around lids lightly with fingertips.

Run a couple of chamomile tea bags under hot water, and then cold. Hold over eyes for at least five minutes.

> **Before you shower or bathe, dry-brush your body with a coarse bath brush. It will slough off dead cells, stimulate circulation, and aid lymphatic drainage. It will de-puff your whole body!**

Instant Color

Cleanse your face, and then take two washcloths, one soaked in hot water, and one in cold. Hold the hot cloth to your face for fifteen seconds, then the cold one for another fifteen seconds. Alternate the hot/cold treatment at least three more times. Your capillaries will expand, improving blood flow, tone, and color.

Using both hands, apply your moisturizer to your face, sweeping up. Gently pinch skin from the cheekbones to the jaw line. Tap on face lightly with fingertips. Do this in an up and down movement from the neck all the way up to the edges of the forehead. Finish by quickly stroking the face with the pads of the fingers from chin to hairline.

Fill a basin with cold water, about twenty ice cubes, and three tablespoons of witch hazel. Splash face about ten times with this mixture.

Put two ice cubes in a plastic bag. Run it over your face several times, until you begin to see some color.

Quick Fixes

Problem: A headache won't go away. Aspirin is not available.

Apply ice to your forehead and hold for about three minutes. If that doesn't work, try rubbing your scalp and temples with gentle but firm strokes.

Problem: You've got a bad case of "hat" hair.

If you can plan ahead when wearing a hat, don't wear too many styling products. After removing your hat, spritz your hair with a little water. Then tousle and shake until all ridges disappear. Back comb your hair gently from ends to roots.

If this still doesn't break a "hat" head, then add a bit of gel, and slick your hair back.

Problem: Your hair has "frozen".

This actually happens to many women in the winter, especially sports enthusiasts. First, don't touch your hair until it thaws. It could actually break off! Then gentle "shake" your head until the style returns to normal.

Problem: Static hair!

If you find your hair catching on to your coat, the walls, or stands on end when you try to brush it, always use a "leave-in conditioner".   If it's too late, slick on a bit of anti-frizz liquid.

Problem: Your feet are aching after a long day.

Add a few drops of eucalyptus or almond oil to your legs and feet. Massage it in, moving your thumbs in small circular motions.

Roll feet around on a bunch of small apples or marbles to ease away knots that come from wearing high heels.

Problem: You've gone too heavy on your powder or foundation.

Just spritz a little water on your face and lightly sponge off with a tissue.

Problem: You've got no time to wash your hair.

Dust it with powder or cornstarch, and brush through.

If your hair is on the shorter, wavier side, take the front section of your hair, dampen it, and divide it into four sections.   Wrap each section around your finger and secure with a clip. Dry hair on a low setting, and you'll have a fresh set of curls.

Tip your hair upside down, spray a spritzer or gel on the undergrowth, and blow dry. This will give your hair new life and movement.

If you're caught in your office, just grab a soda can and wrap your hair around it. Adhere it with an elastic. You probably won't have hairspray in your desk, so grab a bit of perfume (everyone has a small container in their purse) and spritz.

Always carry a big black headband for worst case scenarios. It always looks chic while controlling and smoothing the most unruly hair.

Problem: Those roots have popped up and there's no time to color!

Run to the nearest box of chalk, and find a color that most closely matches. Don't use crayons, they're very hard to shampoo.

If you have black or brown hair use a matching mascara on the roots.

There are sticks at beauty supply stores that also do the job. Try to plan for those in-between times.

Problem: Big under-eye circles

Apply concealer at least a half shade light AFTER applying foundation. Mix a bit of blue eye shadow with a moisturizer. Follow with foundation.

Problem: Tired eyes

Use navy mascara in place of the traditional black. You probably don't keep navy mascara around, so just rub black mascara into that old blue eye shadow (yes, you should have thrown it away years ago, but it's somewhere in the back of your cosmetic drawer), and apply to lashes.

Soft colors like taupe and pink are better for tired eyes than strong dark tones.

Blue liner applied inside of the bottom lid makes the whites of the eyes appear much brighter.

Problem: You've applied your eye liner with too heavy a hand.

Soften the look by applying eye shadow over the liner in a coordinating color. Blend together with a Q-tip.

If you use liner above and below the eye, make sure the two lines don't meet or it will make the eye look too small.

Problem: Your skin is red

If your problem is just a red nose, a little extra concealer in a darker tone will relieve it. Shade down the sides with a darker foundation to take away any puffiness.

If your face is red from a bad sunburn, smooth on a lotion that contains at least 70 per cent aloe vera, or apply a teething ring to the face.

To further neutralize redness, apply a yellow-based foundation with a bronzing powder.

Rub a strawberry over the redness.

Problem: You've spritzed on too much perfume.

You can dilute too much fragrance by taking a warm, soapy washcloth to the pulse points. Always apply scent to the skin, not to clothing.

Problem: Nail polish has turned nails yellow.

Apply a little white vinegar to the nail.
To stop this from happening again, always use a clear top coat that contains
UV absorbers (it should indicate this on the bottle).

Problem: You've lost a button.
The button is loose or hanging.

If you're caught at a restaurant, whisper to the waiter that you need him to retrieve a garbage bag tie from the kitchen. Strip down all the plastic until there's just metal. Thread the button with the metal strip.

Use a binder clasp if the button you lost was brass.

Problem: You've lost your cufflinks.

Make a new pair with binder clasps from your office. Everyone will ask you where you purchased those expensive brass "links".

Use a pair of earrings.

Problem: There's no time for a manicure.

If your polish is just chipped, dip a cotton swab with polish remover. Pat over the chipped area to smooth it out. Touch up the area with a matching polish. Dry quickly by running the nail under very cold water.

Problem: Your nail polish has become dull.

Coat your nail polish with a bit of olive oil. Rub it into your cuticles.

Problem: You don't have time for a face-lift.

Beat one egg white until frothy. Apply to face and neck and allow to dry.

Tape your face with surgical tape sold in beauty supply stores. Adhere it to the skin with spirit gum. Movie stars do it all the time.

Problem: You're wearing a strapless dress, and you need to remove strap marks.

Cover up lines with a tinted moisturizer or a foundation that is one shade darker than your skin tone. Use a sponge and build up the color gradually or evenly.

Problem: You're in a hurry, and can't start from scratch.

Don't take off any makeup if you're rushed, just intensify what's already there.
 Concentrateon retouching.
 Dot on concealer sparingly.
Use a Q-tip to smooth out eye shadow creases.
Add a touch of white or ivory to the brow bone.
Comb eyelashes (lash combs are available at beauty supply shops) and apply more mascara.
Brush eyebrows and line with a soft pencil.
Add bronzing powder to contour areas (jaw, cheeks, sides of nose).
Apply lip liner over existing lipstick and powder over.
Line lids again with a darker color.

Problem: Eyebrows are too dark.

Go over eyebrows with concealer or a light shadow.

Problem: You're out of concealer.

Apply an extra coating of foundation.
Use an ivory eye shadow.

Problem: You've got sweaty palms.

Use a liquid or gel antiperspirant on your palms. Let dry. A spray works better than a roll-on. A powdery spray takes only seconds to dry.

If you are in an office, spray on a little perfume. The alcohol will absorb the perspiration in a pinch.

A small amount of talc will also work.

Problem: Static cling

Run a metal hanger over your panty hose, under your skirt or blouse, or even your hair. The metal will neutralize the electrical charge.

Problem: You need to wash and dry your panty hose in a hurry.

Wash them in shampoo, and whirl them in a salad spinner to get rid of all excess water.

Dry them with a 1600 watt hair dryer.

Problem: Your pants are too tight to tuck in.

Fake a tucked-in look by tying a piece of string around a sweater and pulling the top over what will be a "makeshift" waistband.

Problem: Your shirt keeps popping out.

Tuck your shirt into your panty hose.

Problem: Stains

White chalk covers stain on white and light colored fabrics. Colored chalk is good for all colors.

For an unyielding stain, cover it with a decorative pin.

If there's time, sew on appliqués, use Velcro sequin decorations.

Problem: Too-tight waist

Secure a rubber band around the button, pull through button hole, and loop remainder back on button. You'll need to camouflage this by wearing a belt or long top.

Problem: Skirts that won't lie down!

Make a small incision in the underside of the hem, and drop in a few pennies. The weight will help keep the skirt down and lie flat.

Problem: A blouse or jacket gaps open.

Use double sided tape to hold together.

Problem: Shoes are too big and slide.

Line the shoe with a paper towel or piece of tissue folded in thirds.

Problem: You need to shorten a necklace.

Shorten to desired length, loop a small safety pin through the links and fasten.
Tuck the dangling ends into the back of the shirt.

Problem: A skirt is too long.

Roll over the waistband until the desired length is reached.
Keep it from rolling down by belting it.

Problem: Bloodshot eyes

Use blue colors to take away from the redness. Always stay clear from anything
in the brown tones. Brown carries a strong red pigment.

Problem: Pierced earrings are too heavy.

Take the eraser off a pencil and push it through the stem. It will hold the earring steady.

Problem: Chapped lips

Wet down lips with petroleum jelly. Remove flakiness with a toothbrush.

Chapter Seventeen

Questions

Miscellaneous Questions

Whenever I am interviewed, lecture, or making appearances, there is a consistency to the questions I am asked. Here is a sampling of the most frequently ask beauty and fashion questions.

How do I grow out my bangs?

Have your stylist add a few more long layers around the face. This will help bangs blend in subtly as they grow. The ends should be angled. Be patient, because it can take up to a year for bangs to grow to chin length.

How do I refresh my makeup? If I add more powder it looks too cakey and streaky.

Don't add more makeup until you've sprayed your face with some mineral water or toner. Then separate a tissue, and gently blot with both pieces. Your face will no longer have that "old" look, and you can add a bit more concealer, blush, etc. on a fresher looking face.

I'm not sure how much of my lips to color. I hate that "overdrawn" look.

Form your lips into an "O" shape. Your lipstick should go right to the edges with no gaps.

What's a good way to line eyes?

Look down into a mirror, and pull lid taut. Draw a line as close to the lashes as possible. Start at the top center of the lid and go back and forth in short strokes. Be sure to go all the way to the outer lid with a final stroke pointing up, rather than down.

How do I make large pores look smaller?

After cleansing your face, apply a toner to tighten pores. Use oil-free foundation, making sure to blend evenly. Pat on powder using a large puff for the most even coverage.

I can't seem to handle a lash curler. Are there any other ways to curl my lashes.

A lot of makeup artists prefer to use a spoon to curl lashes. Take the spoon and use to gently bend lashes back. Keep lashes bent for about 30 to 45 seconds.

How can I prevent my nails from chipping?

Always apply a strengthening top coat the day after a new manicure. Continue to apply another coat every other day until your next manicure.

I'm a senior level executive and need to look highly polished and professional, but my wardrobe is very boring. How do I look smart without looking "stiff"?

You need to add some lighter colors and softer cuts and fabrics to your wardrobe. A dress with a matching jacket is a softer alternative to the traditional suit. Also consider wearing a tailored dress. With the right accessories, it can look professional and feminine.

Why do I always break out in red bumps after I shave my legs?

Try exfoliating your legs with a coarse washcloth or loofah before shaving.

How do I make my fragrance last longer?

Start by "layering" your scent. Start with a scented shower or bath in your fragrance. Next, apply perfumed body lotion. Finish by apply perfume or parfum to your pulse points.

What is a safe way to straighten naturally curly hair?

Use a jumbo curling iron, and keep its temperature at about 100 degrees. If your iron doesn't have temperature dial, don't keep it so hot that you recoil upon touching it.

How much should I pay for a moisturizer?

Head to your local drugstore and start reading the labels. You'll be shocked to see that the inexpensive brands have the same ingredients as your pricey favorites. There is no reason to spend more than $15 on a good moisturizer.

How can I make my eyes look pretty without shadow?

Apply foundation one or two shades darker than your regular foundation. Finish with black mascara.

How do I grow out a perm?

Have it cut in long layers, trimming the most damaged parts.

How can I make my eye shadows look less "fake"?

Use cream to powder versions. They don't require an exact application.

When I line my eyebrows they look very harsh.

To get a more natural look, avoid using any eyebrow liner. Switch to an eye shadow in your brow's color or slightly darker.

I like the look of "smoky" eyes, but I tend to overdo it.

The look of black rimmed eyes belongs on the runways. Use your eyeshadow as a liner by wetting it. It will stay on longer than other eye liners, and will give a much softer look.

Can eating gelatin help grow nails?

Eating a well-balanced diet is all you need to think about. Make sure you're getting enough calcium everyday.

Will cutting my hair make it grow faster?

No, just cutting your hair will not make it grow, but getting regular trims will keep the ends strong and thick. This will make it appear that your hair is longer and stronger.

Why does a perfume smell great on my sister and terrible on me?

Your body chemistry reacts to perfume in a unique way. There are other factors to consider as well; such as diet, medication, even the weather. Always test a fragrance, then walk around for about 20 minutes before making a purchasing decision.

How do I get rid of flaky skin?

Be sure to exfoliate your skin at least three times a week. This will remove all the dead surface cells that accumulate, and give you a smooth surface on which to apply your makeup.

What goes on first, concealer or foundation?

This is a personal choice, but it looks more natural when mixing concealer with a little bit of foundation.

Is it okay to wear open-toed shoes in winter?

It's perfectly all right to wear open-toed shoes as long as you're wearing completely sheer hose, and a special occasion dress.

Why do I get tiny white bumps on my arms?

People with dry skin or eczema tend to get these bumps, which are caused by hair follicles that become clogged with oil and dead skin. When you notice them, apply an acid based body moisturizer. This will help clear out the pores.

Why is my hair color changing?

It could be your water. If you've moved recently, you may have gone from soft to hard water. Hard water can cause blonde hair to take on a greenish cast, while causing brown hair to turn red.

What's the best way to add volume to flat hair?

Let hair air-dry, then roll it up in large Velcro rollers. Spray with a volumizer and blow dry over the rollers.

How do I prevent lipstick on my teeth?

After applying your lipstick, wrap your finger around a tissue. Put your lips into an "O" position, stick your finger into your mouth, pulling out slowly. The lipstick that would have landed on your teeth is now on your tissue.

I like the look of leggings, but I don't have right legs. What can I do?

Wear a stretch pant that contains a combination of wood, cotton, rayon, and lycra. It will hold you in without emphasizing bulges.

What do I do with shampoos I don't like?

Use them as bath gels. They'll do the job AND clean your tub too.

I like nude hose but my legs don't look good in them.

The secret is to match the color of the hose to your arms. Most women choose their hose based on their leg color. This looks too pale, and makes the leg look lighter than the rest of the body.

How do I know where to pluck my eyebrows?

Hold a pencil vertically so that it rests beside your nose. The spot where the pencil meets the brow is where the brow should begin. Tweeze any stray hairs outside of that area.

Besides coffee, is there anything that I can do at work to give me that second wind in mid afternoon?

Revive tired muscles and stimulate blood flow by placing a plastic water bottle on the floor. Take off your shoe and gently roll your foot over it from your heels to toes. Repeat with the other foot.

I'm a large sized woman. What is the best way for me to select slacks?

Stay away from elastic waistbands. They are not flattering. Instead look for a single pleat or flat paneled pant in a fluid fabric.

What can I do to keep my lips from drying out?

Keep yourself hydrated by drinking lots of water. Also, slick a little bit of honey on your lips. Not only is honey rich in moisturizers, but it provides a protective barrier.

Chapter Eighteen

Fabulous Figures

You Can Be Fit & Fabulous

What can I tell you that will be the magic elixir you need to drop the weight that keeps you from getting your body in the shape that you've always dreamed of? Well, I have lots to tell you. To start with, women and men who make their fortunes from their looks are real people. In between photo shoots, movies, and appearances, they like to party, gain a few pounds, and eat well. What they know is how to take care of those extra pounds before they really start to accumulate. There are secrets shared among trainers, agents, and the stars themselves that are the cutting edge of the industry. Please take some of this information and incorporate into your own lifestyle. Make changes gradually, and you will be successful in finally taking charge of your body, your health, and your life.

Dieting is dead!

The idea is to change the way you look at food, so that you'll be healthier and stay thinner. Be intelligent about food, and be certain that whatever you eat you'll end up wearing.

What do you want to weigh?

The weight ranges for men and women have changed recently. Here is the latest chart. Realize that it's not just the pounds, it's how you carry them. If you are continually struggling to reach a weight that's five or ten pounds below what you currently weight, look to the state of your life.

More than food, you will have to decide if that Friday night pizza party is more important than the fit of your jeans. You will need to figure out what that "something" is that keeps you from reaching your goal.

Healthy Weight Ranges for Men & Women

Height	Weight Range
5'0"	97 to 128
5'1"	101-132
5'2"	104-137
5'3"	107-141
5'4"	111-146
5'5"	114-150
5'6"	118-155
5'7"	121-160
5'8"	125-164
5'9"	129-169
5'10"	132-174
5'11"	136-179
6'0"	140-184

Women should try to get to the bottom range of their height.
Heights are indicated without shoes.
Weigh yourself in the morning, before breakfast, without clothing.

Top Secrets

Ice water

You've heard that beauties owe their looks and figures to drinking water....lots of it.
But here's the rest of the story. It's the ice that you put into your water that really
makes the difference. Drinking ice water forces your system to rev up metabolism,
to keep body temperature from dropping. That means if you drink eight 12-ounce
glasses of ice water a day, you will burn up an extra 200 calories.

Drink water consistently throughout the day. By the time you are feeling thirsty,
you are on your way to becoming dehydrated.

What you think of as hunger is very often thirst. If you find it hard to down water in
large quantities, flavor it up with a bit of lemon or lime. Water can provide a feeling
of fullness and help the kidneys and liver do their job.

Spicy Foods

Scientists have discovered that chili, peppers, salsa, mustard, and ginger can actually
raise your metabolic rate. That means you can burn calories much faster; up to 45 per cent
faster than that of a bland diet. How? These foods create a thermogenic burn, meaning
it helps the body to produce heat, thus burning off calories.

Seeds

To maximize your intake of nutrients eat seed-containing fruits and vegetables such as
apples, pears, and bananas, as well as seeds themselves (like sesame or sunflower seeds).
Seeds are a great source of fiber, allowing foods to go through your body quickly.

Herbs that help shed pounds

There are herbs you can add to your diet as supplements, teas, and foods that will help your weight loss program go smoothly. Some can even be sprinkled into your bath.

Alfalfa
Aids digestion and acts as a diuretic. .

Bladderwrack
Improves thyroid function and is a bulk laxative. .

Burdock
Improves fat metabolism and acts as a diuretic.

Cardamom
Improves circulation and digestion. A thermogenic herb.

Cayenne
Improves circulation and digestion. Has thermogenic effects.

Cinnamon
Creates a thermogenic burn.

Dandelion root
Aids fat metabolism by affecting the liver.

Fennel
A diuretic that reduces hunger. Improves energy.

Flax seed
A bulk laxative that helps curb hunger.

Garcinia cambogia
Aids fat metabolism and reduces hunger.

Green tea
Aids fat metabolism and increase energy.

Guar gum
Helps reduce hunger and has a laxative effect.

Hawthorn
Reduces blood fat and improves circulation.

Horsetail
A diuretic and nutritive.

Kola nut
A stimulant that decreases appetite and aids in the metabolism of fat.

Parsley
A diuretic and nutrition aid.

Psyllium
Helps to curb hunger and allow for elimination of wastes from the body.

Senna
An all natural laxative.

Foods for the Skin

A diet for a fabulous you includes foods for great skin!

Blueberries
Promotes healthy collagen for fewer wrinkles. Less constriction of veins and faster healing of bruises.

Carrots
Contains high levels of beta carotene for protection against sun damage

Salmon
Rich in essential fatty acids to keep skin moisturized.

Eggs
High in the amino acid "cystein", necessary for the growth and maintenance of the body's tissues.

Yams
Rich in vitamin A to protect the skin from environmental damage.

Mushrooms
Rich in selenium, an antioxidant that may help lower skin cancer risks.

Yogurt
Contains vitamin B Complex which his essential for smooth, blemish-free skin.

Reasons to Eat Breakfast

1.

You'll have a better day at work. Women who eat breakfast work faster
and more accurately than those who don't. Breakfast eaters are also more creative
in the morning.

2.

It keeps you in shape. Breakfast eaters are slimmer than those who skip breakfast.
They don't reach for doughnuts of croissants at the first coffee break.

3.

You'll have lots of health benefits. Cereal with skimmed milk and fruit will
boost your vitamin intake for under 200 calories.

A butterscotch drop satisfies your sweet

tooth since it lasts about 15 minutes in

your mouth, but it only has 25 calories, and

just a trace of fat.

More Secrets

Don't play that funky music

Don't ever eat a meal to toe-tapping music. Researchers at John Hopkins University found that diners who listened to classical music took three bites a minute versus five bites a minute for rock music. They also enjoyed their meal more thoroughly and felt more satisfied.

Say it with Soy

Adding soy to your diet will add more than just a fabulous figure. Soy is packed with powerful antioxidants which interferes with free radical damage. This is the basis for how fast we age. Soy is another reason to turn to a more vegetarian based diet. Unlike animal proteins, soy beans don't spew scads of damaging free radicals through your body to age your cells. Soy also prevents heart disease and diabetes. Japanese, who eat the most soybean in the world (30 times more than Americans) live longer than anyone. Soy is also reported to cut breast cancer rate and lower blood cholesterol.

Add Flavor, Not Calories

Discover flavored vinegars to add flavor without calories. Use a tablespoon of vinegar to thin down and extend your favorite dressing.

Add salsa to just about any food. It perks up taste buds with little or no fat. Dip vegetables in it, spoon it over scrambled eggs, baked potatoes, and add to salads.

Keep olive oil in a spritzer bottle and add it to salads, vegetables, etc.

Chew Away Tension

Relax your facial muscles, and satisfy your chewing urges by chewing on a raw vegetable. Carrots, celery, apples, and fruits are all good picks.

Satisfy Your Sweet Tooth

When you want something sweet, don't grab a candy bar. Try a natural sweet like grapes, blueberries, or strawberries.

When fruit just won't do, grab a jelly bean. At only six calories each, these fat-free sweeties are one of model's favorite snacks.

Why We Diet

67% to be healthier

21% to look better

6% for a better love life

3% for a better job

3% just don't know

How to Deal with Cravings

Brush your teeth

That awful taste you have in your mouth when restricting your calorie intake can lead to eating. Instead, brush your teeth and tongue with a mint flavored toothpaste. Follow up with a flavored mouth wash. This takes away the taste ordinarily removed with foods.

Do something else

Take a bath or go to a movie. Take a walk or call a friend. Do anything until that hunger feeling goes away. After a while, those cravings will subside.

Drink water

Add a lot of lemons to it to take away that awful empty feeling cravings bring.

Eat bread

Sometimes a single slice of bread will calm nerves and end cravings like no other food can.

Rest

Sometimes we just need to relax for a few minutes. Don't ever try to restore your energy level with food.

Your Refrigerator

Did you know that the refrigerator is opened on the average of 22 times a day?
Since it's such an integral part of our dining plans, here's how to make sure we
don't abuse this appliance.

Tack a mirror on it.
There are mirrors that attach to front of the refrigerator. If you have to face yourself
each time you peek in, it just might wake you up to reality.

Tack on an inspirational note.
Make that note a trigger for your success like "I can do it" or "just a month
to bikini time".

Hang up a picture of what you want to look like
It could be a photo of you at your best, or it could be a picture of your favorite actress.
Or even better, cut your head onto a super model's body.

Triggers to Overeating

Too much variety.....avoid buffets and plan meals ahead.

Distractions......don't read or watch TV while eating.

Social events.......Find something to hold while chatting.

Feelings....Don't try to stuff your feelings with food.
Cry if you need to.

Jump Start Diets

The clock is ticking and there's just a few days to that special event.
Or
You hate the thought of a long diet. You need motivation with quick results.

You can make those five pounds disappear. Stars and models do it all the time.
The point is, if you've put on a few pounds, it's very easy to take it off quickly with these "jump start" techniques.

The Garlic and Papaya Diet
This is the one I use as a natural diuretic when I need to whip someone into shape quickly and safely.

Take two garlic tablets and two papaya tablets before breakfast, lunch, and dinner.
Eat very lightly for two day, while keeping up this regime. Stay away from salts, breads, etc. and stay away from carbonated beverages.
Since this is a super diuretic, stay close to a bathroom!

The Cleansing Diet
Go on a veggie diet for a day or two. Start with tomato juice and a grapefruit for breakfast, then eat an array of greens for lunch and dinner.

The Watermelon Diet
Ann-Margaret reportedly lost 20 pounds by eating several slices of watermelon with spring water for breakfast and lunch along with a regular dinner. She claims to have done it in two weeks.

The Cabbage Diet

This diet has been passed around forever. It's been called the Model's Diet, the Stewardess Diet, and the Dolly Parton Diet. All I can tell you is that no one really knows where it came from, but everyone uses it to lose weight quickly.

Diet Soup Recipe

2 to 3 cubes of bouillon
1 pkg. onion soup mix
3 onions
1 to 2 heads of cabbage
2 to 3 pounds of tomatoes
1 carrot
1 pepper
seasonings to taste

Blanche tomatoes in boiling water for one minute. Then plunge in cold water.
Remove skins, dice, and set aside.
Dissolve soup mix and bouillon in 2 to 3 quarts of water.
Chop and add cabbage, onion, carrot, pepper, and spices.
Add tomatoes.
Bring to a boil and cook for 30 to 40 minutes.
Makes enough soup for 2 days.

Eat all the Diet Soup you want for 7 days along with the following:

Day one: Fruits only
Day two: Vegetables only
Day three: Fruits and vegetables
Day four: 8 bananas and non-fat milk
Day five: 6 ounces of lean poultry or fish and plain rice
Day six: 6 ounces of lean poultry or fish and plain rice.
Day seven: Vegetables and rice.

Chapter Nineteen

Recipes under 200 Calories

Enjoy!

The following recipes are real food, that you'd be proud to serve your friends and family. They are all easy to make with products that are readily available. The problems I encountered when searching out the best recipes, was recipes that were "supposed" to be slimming in most cookbooks were anywhere up to 600 or 700 calories. Some of the recipes I found had 20 or more ingredients. I wouldn't bother to cook if I had that many ingredients. What you'll love about each of the following recipes is that they're a cinch to make, and absolutely delicious! I've tried to include something for everyone's taste. The last thing I would do is to tell you to eat cauliflower if you hate it. There are some of us who just can't end a meal without a "little something" sweet. So enjoy!

Appetizers Under 200 Calories

Hot Spinach Artichoke Dip

Calories: 95 per serving
Makes 24 servings

1 cup grated parmesan cheese
1 cup low fat mayonnaise
1 can (14 ounces) artichoke hearts, drained & chopped
1 package chopped spinach, thawed & drained
2 tablespoons tomato
garlic, salt & pepper to taste

Heat oven to 350 degrees.
Mix all ingredients except tomato.
Spoon into 9-inch plate or quiche dish.
Bake 30 to 35 minutes or until lightly browned.
Serve topped with tomato.

Stuffed Mushrooms

Calories: 41 per serving
Makes 4 servings

12 large mushrooms
2 tablespoons lemon juice, divided
1 small red onion chopped
1 teaspoon dill
2 tablespoons nonfat plain yogurt
1 teaspoon mustard (preferably Dijon)
salt & pepper

Finely chop mushroom stems, leaving caps whole.
Over high heat combine 1 tablespoon lemon juice with 1 quart water.
Bring to boil.
Add mushroom caps and cook until tender.
Transfer to bowl filled with ice water.
Drain and pat dry.
Evenly divide filling among mushroom caps.

Salsa Dip

Calories: 60 per serving
Makes 24 servings

1 pound processed cheese spread
1 eight ounce jar salsa

Microwave cheese spread and salsa in 1 1/2 quart microwave-safe bowl for 5 minutes on high.
Stir after 3 minutes.

Serve with baked tortilla chips, pepper wedges, or baked potato skins.

Creamy Leek Dip

Calories: 65 per serving
Makes 10 servings

2 cups low fat small-curd cottage cheese
1/4 cup skim milk
1 packet leek soup mix
1 cup fresh parsley sprigs

In a food processor fitted with the metal blade, combine all ingredients except parsley sprigs until smooth.

Add parsley and process until it is finely chopped.

Place in a medium bowl and refrigerate for at least 2 hours.

Baked Onion Rings

Calories: 51 per serving
Makes 4 servings

6 tablespoons seasoned dry bread crumbs
1/2 large sweet yellow onion
1 egg white

Preheat oven to 450 degrees.

Slice onion as thinly as possible.
Separate into rings.
Drip onion ring first in egg white, then in crumbs.
Place on a nonstick baking sheet.

Bake 10 minutes.

Crabmeat Spread

28 calories per serving
Makes 12 servings

1 cup crabmeat
1/2 cup celery, diced
1 small onion, diced
1/2 green pepper, diced
1 cup sprouts
1 cup lowfat cottage cheese

Blend all the above ingredients with enough vinegar to moisten.
Season to taste.

Soups Under 200 Calories

Gazpacho

52 calories per serving
Makes 6 servings

2 1/2 cups fresh tomatoes
1 large green pepper, chopped
1 large onion, chopped
1 teaspoon garlic flavoring
1 teaspoon dried chive
1 teaspoon paprika
salt and pepper
1/2 teaspoon sugar
2 cups tomato juice
1 medium-size cucumber, peeled, cut lengthwise, & seeded.
2 tablespoons lemon juice

Shred cucumber with a grater.
In a large bowl, combine tomatoes, pepper, onion, & seasonings.

Stir in remaining ingredient.

Cover & chill at least 2 hours before serving

Yellow Pepper & Orange Soup

35 calories per serving
Makes four servings

Preheat oven to broiler

3 yellow bell peppers halved and seeded
1 large onion, chopped
grated rind and juice of 1 orange
1 1/2 cups chicken stock
4 pitted black olives, chopped
salt and pepper

Place pepper, skin side up, on a baking sheet.
Cook under broiler until the skins are blackened.
Cover and leave to cool.

Place the onion & orange juice in a pan.
Bring to a boil, then cover and simmer for 10 minutes or until the onion is tender.

Peel the peppers. Blend with onion, half the orange rind, and chicken stock until smooth.

Season to taste, then heat gently. Serve sprinkled with olives and remaining rind.

Vichyssoise

149 calories per serving
Makes 6 servings.

3 medium leeks
Cooking spray
3 potatoes, peeled & diced
3 cups chicken broth
2 cups evaporated skim milk
freshly ground pepper

Cut and discard the roots and tough leaves from leeks.
Cut leeks in half lengthwise, and rinse under cold water.
Then cut the leeks crosswise into 1/4 inch thick slices.

Lightly spray a medium-sized saucepan with cooking spray.
Heat the saucepan over medium heat.

Add leeks, cooking and stirring for 5 minutes.
Add potatoes and broth, and bring to boil.

Reduce heat and simmer for 30 minutes.
Transfer leek mixture to food processor.
Blend until smooth.
Stir in milk and pepper.

Soup may be chilled before serving.

Tortellini Soup

105 calories per serving
Makes 4 servings

3 cups beef broth
1 cup frozen cheese tortellini
1 cup frozen peas
2 tablespoons sun-dried tomatoes
1 teaspoon dried basil

In a medium saucepan, combine all ingredients.
Cover and bring to a boil.
Reduce heat and simmer for 5 minutes or until tortellini are tender.

Vegetable Soup

75 calories per serving
Makes 8 servings.

16 ounces tomato juice
16 ounces water
14 ounces canned chicken broth
16 ounces peeled tomatoes
1/2 pound green beans, cut into 1 inch pieces
3/4 pound carrots, sliced
3 celery stalks, sliced
1 onion, sliced
1 small zucchini, sliced
1 summer squash, sliced

Combine tomato juice, water, broth, and tomatoes, and bring to a boil.

Add green beans, carrots, and celery.
Bring to boil and simmer 30 minutes.

Season to taste.

Mixed Bean Soup

95 calories a serving
Makes 4 servings

1 teaspoon olive oil
1 red onion, chopped
1 crushed garlic cloves
2/3 cup tomato paste
1 teaspoon dried thyme
1 1/2 cups frozen or fresh green beans
15 ounce can cannelini beans
salt and pepper to taste

Heat the olive oil and fry the onion and garlic for 10 minutes or until softened but not brown.

Add the paste and thyme and bring to a boil.
Add the green beans, covering and simmering for about 6 minutes or until tender.

Add the beans, and season.

Salads

Greek Salad

90 calories per serving
Makes 2 servings

2 cups romaine lettuce
2 tablespoons feta cheese
1 tomato
1 cucumber
1/2 stalk of celery, sliced
2 black olives
2 tablespoons vinegar
1 tablespoon olive oil

Toss all ingredients together and serve.

German Potato Salad

180 calories per serving
Makes 4 servings

1 1/2 pounds small red potatoes
3 shallots or leeks, minced
1/4 cup parsley, chives, and thyme
2 tablespoons balsamic or wine vinegar
2 tablespoons beef broth
2 tablespoons olive oil
2 minced garlic cloves

Boil potatoes in medium saucepan until tender.
Remove from heat, drain and cut in halves.

In a medium bowl, toss with shallots or leeks, and herbs.
Set aside.

In a small saucepan, combine vinegar, broth, olive oil, and garlic.
Warm over low heat and pour over potatoes.

Fold in carefully before serving.

Red Coleslaw

40 calories per serving
Makes 4 servings

1/2 small red cabbage, shredded
1 red onion, thinly sliced
4 radishes, thinly sliced
1 red apple, cored & grated
1 tablespoon low fat plain yogurt
1 teaspoon honey
salt and pepper to taste

Place the cabbage, onion, radishes, and apple in a salad bowl and toss.

In a screw topped jar, shake the remaining ingredients until they are blended.

Pour the dressing over the salad and toss well.

Couscous Salad

105 calories per serving
Makes 4 servings

1 1/2 cups couscous
1 celery stalk , chopped
1/2 small cauliflower, cut into small florets
4 scallions, chopped
3 tablespoons dried parsley
1 tablespoon lemon juice
1/2 teaspoon chili sauce
salt and pepper to taste

Cook couscous according to package directions. Leave to cool.

Stir in all remaining ingredients, season, and toss.

Spoon onto large platter, and serve.

Deli Salad

180 calories per serving
Makes 8 servings

7 ounce can of artichoke hearts, drained
1 cup cubed mozzarella cheese
1 cup rotini pasta, cooked, and drained
2 1/2 ounce can of pitted olives
1/2 cup low fat Italian dressing
1 cup red onion rings
1/2 cup chopped green pepper
1/4 cup shredded parmesan cheese

Mix together all ingredients.
Refrigerate before serving.

Spinach Salad

80 calories per serving
Makes 4 servings

2 cups fresh spinach
1/2 cup dried apricots, chopped
2 tablespoons sunflower seeds
1 tablespoon sesame seeds
2 tablespoons orange juice
1 tablespoon balsamic vinegar
2 tablespoons low fat plain yogurt
salt and pepper to taste

Place spinach, apricots, and sunflower seeds, in a bowl and toss.

In a small pan, heat sesame seeds gently until they begin to color and pop.
Remove from heat.

Add orange juice, vinegar, and seasoning to pan.

Spoon dressing over salad and serve.

Waldorf Salad

60 calories per serving
Makes 10 servings

6 cups diced apples
2 1/2 cups thinly sliced celery
1/2 cup raisins
1/2 cup non fat mayonnaise
1/4 cup nonfat sour cream

Combine apples, celery, and raisins in a large bowl.
Stir to mix well.

In a small bowl, combine mayonnaise with sour cream, and stir.

Add mayonnaise mixture to apple mixture, and toss together.

Refrigerate for 2 hours before serving.

Chicken and Pasta Salad

165 calories per serving
Makes 8 servings

3 cups chicken broth
approximately 1 pound of boneless chicken breasts
2 cups of shell pasta
1 cup nonfat mayonnaise
1 teaspoon mustard
1/2 teaspoon celery salt
ground pepper
2 ribs celery, thinly sliced
1 cup baby peas, cooked, drained, and cooled
1 cup seedless red grapes, washed and cut in half

Bring chicken broth to a simmer in a medium saucepan.
Add chicken breasts and cook for 20 minutes.

Remove breasts and chill.

Cook pasta according to directions, drain and rinse in cold water.

In a mixing bowl, mix together mayonnaise, mustard, celery salt, and pepper.
Cut chicken into bite-size pieces and add to mixture.
Add pasta, celery, peas, and grapes.
Toss together.

Cover and refrigerate for an hour.

Cucumber Salad with Dill

50 calories per serving
Makes 4 servings

2 cucumbers
3 tablespoons vinegar
1 tablespoon sugar
1 red onion, sliced and made into rings
salt and pepper to taste
2 teaspoons dried dill weed

Wash the cucumbers and partially remove the peel in lengthwise strips. Use a fork to leave a little skin between each strip and slice crosswise.

Combine vinegar, sugar, salt and pepper in a bowl until sugar is dissolved. Add cucumber, onion, and dill and toss well.

Can be served right away.

Vegetable Salad

55 calories per serving
Makes 8 servings

3 cups broccoli, chopped
3 cups cauliflower, chopped
1 cup sliced celery
about 20 pitted black olives, sliced
16 ounce can mushrooms, drained
3/4 cup fat-free Italian salad dressing

Combine all ingredients in a large bowl.
Stir to cover vegetables.

Chill at least 3 hours before serving.

Vegetable Dishes
under 200 Calories

Snow Peas and Carrots

80 calories per serving
Makes 4 servings

1 onion, thinly sliced
4 teaspoons olive oil
2 carrots, cut into 2 inch strips
1/2 pound snow peas, strings removed
2 teaspoons dried dill
salt and pepper to taste

Microwave onion and oil for 1 minute.

Stir in carrots, cover with plastic, and microwave, 2 minutes.

Stir in snow peas and dill.
Microwave covered for 6 minutes.
Let stand for 3 minutes.
Season and serve.

Carrots and Grapes

45 calories per serving
Makes 4 servings

2 cups sliced carrots
1 shallot, chopped
1/4 cup water
2 tablespoons red wine vinegar
1 tablespoon brown sugar
1/2 cup halved seedless grapes

Cook carrots and shallot in water in nonstick skillet about 10 minutes.
Stir until carrots are tender.
Push carrot mixture to side of skillet.
Stir in vinegar and sugar.
Toss all together.

Potato Skins with Salsa

49 calories per serving
Makes 16 servings

Preheat oven to 450 degrees

4 baking potatoes
8 ounce container plain non-fat yogurt
1 small tomato, chopped
1/2 cup black beans, drained and rinsed
1/2 teaspoon ground cumin
1/2 cup shredded reduced-fat cheddar cheese

Prick potatoes and bake until tender (about an hour).
Cool 15 minutes.
Quarter potatoes lengthwise.

Scoop out flesh, leaving the shells intact.

Place skins on baking sheet coated with cooking spray.
Sprinkle with salt and pepper.

Combine tomato, beans, scallion, and cumin in a bowl.

Sprinkle skins with cheese.
Bake until cheese melts (about a minute).
Top skins with salsa.
Serve with yogurt.

Zucchini Frittata

65 calories per serving
Makes 4 servings

2 small zucchini
1 teaspoon water
2 green onions, chopped
1 teaspoon dried basil
1/2 teaspoon dried marjoram
1 1/2 cups egg substitute
2 tablespoons parmesan cheese

Cut each zucchini lengthwise into quarters.
Thinly slice each quarter.

Place the water in a 10 inch skillet.
Add zucchini and onions.
Cook over low heat about 3 minutes.
Discard cooking liquid.
Stir in basil and marjoram

Carefully pour egg substitute over zucchini and onions.
Cook over low heat until mixture starts to set.
Lift edges of uncooked mixture to flow underneath.
Continue cooking until nearly set and sprinkle with cheese.

Broil about 1 minute and serve.

Peas and Onions

105 calories per serving
Makes 8 servings

16 ounce package of frozen small whole onions
2 tablespoons butter
20 ounces of frozen peas, thawed
2 tablespoons chopped mint
1 tablespoon parmesan cheese
salt and pepper to taste

Cook onions according to directions on package.
Drain

Melt butter in skillet and cook 3 minutes.
Add onions and peas.

Place in bowl and toss with mint, cheese, and salt & pepper.

Rosemary "Fries"

75 calories per serving
Makes 4 servings

Preheat broiler.

3 large baking potatoes
2 teaspoons olive oil
1 teaspoon rosemary
salt and pepper

Cut potatoes lengthwise into 3 slices each.
Cut each slice into 3 large French fries.
Cook potatoes in microwave with a bit of water.
Take out while still crisp and not mashing soft.

Spread steamed potatoes on baking sheet sprayed with a cooking spray.
Sprinkle with dried rosemary.
Broil until potatoes are golden brown.
Turn and brown other side.
Season and serve.

Glazed Carrots

70 calories per serving
Makes 4 servings

1 pound carrots
1 cup water
4 teaspoons apple juice
1 tablespoon brown sugar
1 teaspoon butter
1/2 teaspoon nutmeg

Cut carrots into 2-inch pieces, then quarter pieces lengthwise.
Microwave carrots for 5 minutes until just tender.

Meanwhile, stir together apple juice, sugar, and butter.
Microwave for about 30 seconds or until brown sugar and butter are just melted.
Drizzle carrots with apple juice mixture.
Toss to coat.
Serve sprinkled with nutmeg.

Baked Onions

160 calories per serving
Makes 6 servings

Preheat oven to 350 degrees

6 medium onions
3 strips bacon cut into 1 inch pieces
1/2 pepper, diced
1 small carrot, diced
1 cup fresh bread crumbs (3 slices bread)
1/8 teaspoon dried parsley
2 tablespoons melted butter
salt and pepper
1 cup water
1/2 cup beef broth

Bring a large pot of water to boil.
Cut off 1 end of each onion.
Scoop out onion centers, leaving 1/2 inch shells.
Chopo 1/2 cup scooped out onion.
Discard remainder.
Add shells to boiling water and cook 15 minutes.
Remove and drain.

In small skillet cook bacon, pepper, carrot, and onion til tender.
Combine bacon mixture with bread crumbs, parsley, butter, salt & pepper.

Divide stuffing among onions and place in baking dish.
Pour water and broth into dish.
Bake, uncovered, until onions are tender (about 2 hours).

Rice Almondine

115 calories per serving
Makes 6 servings

1 cup chopped onion
1 1/4 cups chicken broth
1 tablespoon lemon juice
1/2 teaspoon garlic powder
1 1/2 cups minute brown rice
1 cup frozen green beans, thawed
2 tablespoons toasted slivered almonds
1/2 teaspoon dried dill weed.

Spray cooking spray in medium saucepan.
Add onion and cook until tender.
Add broth, lemon juice, and garlic powder.
Bring to boil.
Stir in rice and return to boil.
Reduce heat to low.
Cover and simmer about 5 minutes.

Remove from heat.
Stir in beans, almonds, and dill.
Cover and let stand 5 minutes.
Fluff with fork and serve.

Swiss Asparagus Au Gratin

170 calories per serving
Makes 4 servings

Heat oven to 400 degrees.

1/2 cup water
1 1/2 pounds asparagus spears, trimmed
1/2 cup Swiss cheese, shredded
1/4 cup bread crumbs
2 tablespoons butter, melted
1/2 teaspoon dry mustard
1/4 teaspoon fresh ground pepper

Bring 1/2 cup water to boil in 10 inch skillet.
Add asparagus.
Cook 2 minutes and drain.
Place in 10 x 6 inch baking pan.
Mix remaining ingredients and sprinkle over asparagus.

Bake 10 minutes or until cheese mixture is lightly browned.

Entrees Under 200 Calories

Broiled Flank Steak

170 calories per serving
Makes 4 servings

1 pound lean flank steak
3/4 cup dry red wine
3 garlic cloves, cut into quarters
a bay leaf, cut in half
1 teaspoon onion powder
2 teaspoons Dijon mustard

Preheat broiler.

Marinate steak in a baking dish with wine, garlic, and bay leaf for 1 hour.
Drain steak.
Place steak on a broiler rack; sprinkle with onion powder.
Spread a thin layer of mustard over top.
Broil to desired doneness.

Pineapple Steak Kabobs

185 calories per serving
Makes 4 servings

1 tablespoon soy sauce
2 tablespoons water
1 teaspoon garlic powder
1 tablespoon applesauce

1 pound flank steak, cut into 2-inch squares
small red bell pepper, cut in 1-inch squares
8 ounce can unsweetened pineapple chunks, juice reserved
8 fresh mushrooms

Combine soy sauce, water, garlic powder and applesauce.
Marinate this mixture over steak for 1 hour.

Thread flank steak, pepper, pineapple chunks, and mushrooms on skewers.
Broil until desired doneness.

Pork Steaks with Peppercorn Glaze

175 calories per serving
Makes 4 servings

4 lean pork loin steaks
1 tablespoon green peppercorns, crushed
4 tablespoons balsamic vinegar
1 cup chicken broth
4 scallions, sliced

Mix together peppercorns and vinegar.
Sprinkle over pork.
Let sit for 30 minutes.

Reserving the peppercorn mixture, fry the pork in a non-stick pan.

Add the peppercorn mix, broth, and scallions.
Boil rapidly, uncovered, for about 10 minutes.

Lemon Chicken

130 calories per serving
Makes 4 servings

Preheat oven to 350 degrees.

1 pound boneless chicken breast halves
2 lemons
1 teaspoon dried tarragon
fresh pepper

Place chicken in foil-lined baking pan
Fold sides of the foil up.

Halve lemons and squeeze juice of 1/2 lemon over each chicken piece.
Sprinkle each piece with 1/4 teaspoon tarragon and pepper.

Fold foil together and seal to secure chicken.

Bake for about 45 minutes.

Mediterranean Turkey Spirals

125 calories per serving
Makes 4 servings

4 thin turkey breast steaks
2 tablespoons pesto
1/2 cup basil leaves
1/2 cup chicken broth
1 cup tomato juice
garlic salt
pepper

Beat turkey until thin.
Spread with pesto sauce.
Lay basil leaves over each steak, then roll like a jelly roll.
Secure with toothpicks.

Combine broth and tomato juice.
Bring to a boil over high heat.
Add the turkey spirals, cover and simmer for 15 minutes.

Season and remove toothpicks.
Serve hot.

RECIPES UNDER 200 CALORIES

Turkey Meat Loaf

175 calories per serving
Makes 8 servings

Preheat oven to 350 degrees

1 1/2 pounds ground turkey breast
1/2 cup seasoned bread crumbs
1/2 cup uncooked oatmeal
1/2 cup ketchup
1/2 cup low-fat milk
2 tablespoons soy sauce
1 large onion, chopped
1 egg
fresh ground pepper

In a large bowl, combine all ingredients.
Place mixture in a loaf pan coated with cooking spray.
Bake about 1 1/4 hours.
Meat should not have any pink color remaining.

Baked Scallops

125 calories per serving
Makes 4 servings

Preheat oven to 450 degrees.

1 tablespoon butter
1/4 cup white wine
juice of one lemon
1 pound scallops

Heat all but the scallops in oven.
Pour liquid over rinsed scallops.
Marinate for 20 minutes at room temperature.
Bake for about 5 minutes.
Do not overcook.

Oysters Rockefeller

90 calories per serving
Makes 4 servings

Preheat broiler

2 teaspoons olive oil
1 tablespoons grated onion
tarragon, pepper, and Tabasco sauce to taste
10 ounces frozen chopped spinach, thawed and drained
8 ounces oysters, raw or canned
2 tablespoons grated mozzarella cheese
1 tablespoon Parmesan cheese

Combine bread crumbs, oil, onion, and seasoning.
Toss mixture with spinach.

Broil oysters for 5 to 7 minutes if using raw.
Drain liquid if using canned.

Top oysters with spinach mixture and broil about 4 minutes.
Sprinkle with cheeses and broil until just melted.

Deviled Shrimp

140 calories per serving
Makes 1 serving

5 jumbo shrimp, uncooked, peeled and deveined
2 tablespoons white wine
1 tablespoon Dijon mustard
1 crushed garlic clove
1/4 cup onions, diced
salt & pepper to taste
1 tomato, peeled
1/4 cup chopped parsley

Coat skillet with cooking spray.
Add shrimp, and cook about 2 minutes on each side.
Add wine, mustard, garlic, onion, and seasonings.
Cover and cook about 8 minutes.
Add tomato, breaking it up with a fork.
Mix all together, cover again, and cook 10 minutes.
Add parsley and serve.

Seafood Bisque

130 calories per serving
Makes 8 servings

2 1/2 cups frozen corn, thawed
2 cups chicken broth
1 tablespoon butter
2 peppers, chopped
salt & pepper
1 cup low fat milk
1/2 pound shrimp, peeled & deveined
1/2 pound scallops
3 tablespoons parsley

In food processor combine 2 cups corn with 1 cup chicken broth
Puree until smooth
Melt butter over medium heat in saucepan.
Add peppers, onions, salt, and pepper to taste.
Cook 5 minutes.
Stir in corn mixture, milk, and remaining broth.
Cover and simmer 5 minutes. Add shrimp, scallops, remaining corn, & parsley.
Cook about 5 minutes and serve.

Baked Eggplant, Tomatoes, and Feta

95 calories per serving
Makes 4 servings

Preheat oven to 400 degrees

1 medium eggplant, thinly sliced
2 large tomatoes, sliced
1 cup crumbled feta cheese
4 tablespoons plain yogurt
olive oil
paprika
garlic salt

Sprinkle the eggplant slices with garlic salt, leave for 30 minutes, then wipe off.

Spray baking dish with cooking spray.
Arrange eggplant & tomatoes to slightly overlap.
Sprinkle with feta cheese and spoon over yogurt.

Sprinkle with paprika and garlic salt.
Bake for 30 minutes or until bubbling & golden.

Vegetarian Stuffed Peppers

145 calories per serving
Makes 6 servings

Preheat oven to 375 degrees

6 peppers
2 cups cooked rice
1 cup couscous
3 egg whites
salt & pepper to taste
parsley to taste
1/4 cup seasoned bread crumbs
1 small onion, chopped
1/2 cup chopped celery
8 ounce can tomato sauce

Cut peppers in half and remove seeds.
Microwave 2 minutes.

Combine rice, cooked couscous, egg whites, and seasonings.
Sprinkle in bread crumbs and set aside.

Bring 1 cup water to boil.
Add onion & celery and boil 15 more minutes.
Add tomato sauce, mix and cook 20 minutes.

Spray a baking dish with cooking spray.
Fill peppers with stuffing.
Cover with sauce.
Bake for 40 minutes.

Breads, Pizza, Quiche

under

200 Calories

Lemon Pepper Popovers

105 calories per serving
Makes 6 servings

Preheat oven to 450 degrees.

1 cup flour
1 cup skim milk at room temperature
1 tablespoon olive oil
salt & pepper to taste
2 teaspoons lemon zest
3 egg whites, slightly beaten

Mix together flour and milk.
Add remaining ingredients, only enough to mix.

Grease muffin cups with cooking spray.
Fill each cup half full.

Bake 15 minutes at 450 degrees.
Reduce heat to 350 degrees for 20 more minutes.
Serve at once.

Blueberry Muffins

123 calories per serving
Makes 12 muffins

Preheat oven to 400 degrees.

2 cups flour
1 tablespoon baking powder
1/2 teaspoon salt
1 cup blueberries
4 egg whites
1 1/2 cups nonfat yogurt
1/2 cup sugar
1 teaspoon vanilla extract

Mix together flour, baking powder and salt.
Add blueberries.
Stir lightly to coat & set aside.

Beat egg whites to peaks.
Add yogurt, sugar, and vanilla.

Add liquid mixture to dry ingredients and fold together gently.

Bake in nonstick 12 cup muffin pan.

Optional: place 1 blueberry in center of each muffin
Sprinkle a little sugar over each muffin.

Bake for 20 minutes.

Spiced Carrot Bread

125 calories per serving
Makes one loaf/12 slices

Preheat oven to 350 degrees.

2 eggs
4 tablespoons vegetable oil
3 tablespoons sugar
3 carrots, coarsely grated
1 1/3 flour
1 teaspoon baking powder
2 teaspoons allspice
3 tablespoons skim milk

Line loaf pan with wax paper.

Mix together eggs, oil, and sugar.
Stir in carrots.
Add flour, baking powder, and allspice.
Fold in milk.

Pour into pan.
Bake 40 to 45 minutes.

Spicy Onion Tart

175 calories per serving

Preheat oven to 375 degrees.

1 tablespoon butter
4 large yellow onions
1 cup nonfat sour cream
3 eggs
black & cayenne pepper to taste
salt to taste
one frozen pie shell
1 teaspoon dried parsley

Melt butter in large non-stick skillet.
Add onions.
Cover and cook 15 minutes.
Uncover and cook until browned.

Remove from heat and let cool.

Combine sour cream, eggs, peppers and salt.
Add onions.
Pour into shells.
Sprinkle with parsley.
Bake 30 to 35 minutes.
Cool slightly before slicing.

Quick Pizza

95 calories per serving
Makes 2 servings

1 large pita bread
4 tablespoons pasta sauce
4 tablespoons low-fat cottage cheese
1/4 teaspoon dried oregano
1/2 teaspoon Parmesan cheese

Split bread in half horizontally.
Broil until lightly toasted.
Cover each half with sauce.
Follow with cottage cheese.
Sprinkle with oregano and cheese.

Broil until cheese melts.

Desserts under 200 Calories

Lemon Bars

150 calories per serving
Makes 24 bars

Preheat oven to 350 degrees

1 cup light shortening
1 cup brown sugar
1 1/2 cups flour
1 teaspoon baking powder
1 teaspoon cinnamon
1 cup quick-cooking oats
8 ounces light cream cheese, softened
1/2 cup sugar
1/2 cup lemon juice
2 teaspoons grated lemon peel

Beat together shortening & sugar.
Add flour, baking powder, & cinnamon.
Stir in oats.

Reserve 1 1/2 cups oat mixture.
Press remaining oat mixture onto bottom of greased 13 x 9 inch pan.

Beat cream cheese with sugar, juice, & peel.
Pour over oat mixture.
Sprinkle with remaining mixture.
Bake about 30 minutes.

Apple Crisp

135 calories per serving
Makes 8 servings

Preheat oven to 375 degrees

4 sliced apples
1/3 cup brown sugar
1/4 cup flour
1/4 cup rolled oats
1 teaspoon cinnamon
2 tablespoons butter, softened

Spray an 8 x 8 inch pan with cooking spray.
Place apple slices in pan.
Mix remainng ingredients together and sprinkle over apples.

Bake 30 minutes.

Applenut Cookies

75 calories each
Makes 14 cookies

Preheat oven to 400 degrees

1 1/2 cups rolled oats
1 teaspoon allspice
4 tablespoons shortening
3 tablespoons brown sugar
1 apple, cored and chopped
3 tablespoons walnuts
1 egg white

Mix together oats, spice, and shortening.

Add sugar, apple, nuts and egg white.
Stir.

Form into 14 balls.
Arrange on non-stick baking pan.
Flatten slightly.
Bake for 12 minutes.

Chocolate Truffles

60 calories per truffle

1/2 cup chopped raisins
2 tablespoons flavored liqueur
40 squares graham crackers
14 ounce can sweetened condensed skim milk
1/2 cup unsweetened cocoa powder
1 teaspoon vanilla

Combine raisins & liqueur
Let stand until softened.

Combine ground graham crackers, milk, 1/4 cup cocoa powder, vanilla, & raisins.
Chill one hour.

Place remaining cocoa powder in shallow bowl.
Shape chocolate mixture into balls.
Roll in cocoa powder.
Freeze 15 minutes.
Store in refrigerator.

Biscotti

65 calories per cookie

Preheat oven to 350 degrees.

3 cups flour
1 teasoon baking powder
5 tablespoons shortening
2/3 cup sugar
3 eggs
1 tablespoon lemon juice
1 cup currants
3/4 cup dried apricots

Combine flour & baking powder.
Set aside.

Cream together sugar and shortening.
Beat eggs in.
Add lemon juice.
Add dry ingredients.
Add currants and apricots.

Divide & shape dough into 2 loaves
Bake 30 minutes.

Cheesecake Cups

129 calories per serving
Makes 8 servings

Preheat oven to 375 degrees.

1 quart plain lowfat yogurt
3 tablespoons sugar
1 teaspoon lemon juice
2 slices pumpernickel bread
2 tablespoons honey
1 cup mandarin orange sections

Strain yogurt and & refrigerate 4 hours.
Stir in lemon juice & sugar
Refrigerate another 4 hours.

Toast bread, crumble, and add honey.
Press into bottom of 8 cups to make crust
Cover with yogurt mixture.
Add a couple of oranges on top.

Serve.

Fruit Skewers with Mango Puree

80 calories per serving
Makes 4 servings

1 ripe mango, peeled, pitted, and chopped
1 tablespoon lime juice
1/2 cored pineapple
1 papaya peeled and seeded
2 kiwi, peeled and quartered

Place the mango and lime juice in a food processor and blend til smooth.

Cut pineapple and papaya into bite-sized chunks and three on 4 bamboo skewers with kiwi.

To serve, spoon a little mango puree on to 4 plates.
Place skewer on top.

Molasses Cookies

50 calories per serving
Makes 40 cookies

Preheat oven to 350 degrees

1/2 cup light molasses
1/3 cup shortening
2 cups flour
1/4 cup brown sugar
1 tablespoon skim milk
1 teaspoon ginger
1/2 teaspoon baking powder

Heat molasses to boiling & stir in shortening til melting.
Remove from heat and stir in flour, sugar, milk, ginger, & baking powder.
Stir until mixture pulls away from pan.

After dough cools, form into 1 inch thick log.
Refrigerate until firm.

Slice into 1/4 inch slices.
Place on non-stick cookie sheet.
Bake about 10 minutes.

A Final Word

It is my sincere hope that you will use this book to take charge of your life and your looks. But the point I make to you in my closing words is this: No amount of makeup or clothing will make you beautiful. The REAL secret to beauty is to live life with passion and compassion. Love as hard as you can, and yes, even allow yourself to feel the pain that will come to all of us.

There is no amount of makeup that will mask the life you've led. Let the spirit of your face show that you've lived your life with grace and courage. Don't be afraid to try something new, to reinvent yourself every single day you are here on earth. Don't let your looks rule your every waking minute. The true key to beauty is do the best you can and respect yourself as much as you expect others to respect you. Learn to make the best of what you've been given because you owe it to yourself. Then go on. Go on to all the other adventures of your life.

> **"For beauty is but the spirit breaking through the skin."**
>
> **Rodin**
> **Painter/Sculptor**

About the Author

Diane Irons started modeling at the age of fourteen. Just the way other kids collected baseball cards, Diane collected tips and advice from the beautiful women she worked with. After college, Diane Irons became a leading journalist in the TV, Radio, and Newspaper industries.

Combining her reporting skills with her knowledge of beauty, fashion, and fitness, she has dedicated herself to finding what REALLY works for women, and how to avoid being ripped off.

Diane Irons has lent her expertise on the nation's top shows, and she is continually in demand by the most prestigious publications in the world.

Still modeling after over thirty years in the business, Diane Irons teaches us that beauty knows no age, size, or boundaries.

Index

Recipe Index

Desserts under 200 Calories

ORDER FORM

Additonal copies of "Secret Beauty" available at $15.95 & $4.00 shipping and handling.

Name:_____

Address:_____

City:_____ State:_____

Zip code_____Telephone:_____

Make checks payable to: International Image Press
196 Main Street
Wakefield, MA 01880-1823

Charge by Visa:_____ Mastercard:_____

Number:_____

Expiration date:_____

Name on Card:_____

Or Order by Phone!

Call Toll Free 24 Hours a Day! Seven Days a Week!

1-800-230-9959

To communicate with the author write:

Diane Irons
c/o International Image
196 Main Street
Wakefield, MA 01880